S0-BCP-884

THE GREAT SCIENTISTS

THE GREAT SCIENTISTS

1

Abano-Banting

Edited by
FRANK N. MAGILL

GROLIER EDUCATIONAL CORPORATION
Danbury, Connecticut

∞ The paper used in these volumes conforms to the American National Standard for Permanence of Paper for Printed Library Materials, Z39.48-1984.

Library of Congress Cataloging-in-Publication Data
The great scientists / edited by Frank N. Magill.
p. cm.
Includes bibliographical references.
ISBN 0-7172-7134-X (set)
1. Scientists—Biography. I. Magill, Frank Northen. 1907-
Q141.G767 1989
509.2'2—dc20
[B] 89-17165
CIP

Picture Research: Imagefinders, Inc., Washington, D.C.

Second Printing

Published 1989 by
Grolier Educational Corporation
Danbury, Connecticut, 06816

PRINTED IN THE UNITED STATES OF AMERICA

PUBLISHER'S NOTE

The Great Scientists surveys some four hundred exceptional and renowned thinkers and practitioners in the sciences, both worldwide and across time. Countries represented include France, Germany, the Soviet Union, Poland, Italy, England, the United States, Australia, Sweden, Austria, India, Switzerland, the Netherlands, Greece, and Egypt; scientists from the ancient Egyptian Imhotep (twenty-seventh century B.C.) to the twentieth century Nobel Prize laureate Linus Pauling are included.

The purpose of this twelve-volume set, covering scientists both in the "hard" and in the social sciences, is to provide broad biographical coverage of significant figures in the sciences in a ready-reference format. Among the subject areas represented are the disciplines of anthropology, archaeology, astronomy, biology, botany, chemistry, earth science, economics, engineering, geography, human sexuality, invention and technology, mathematics, medicine, natural history, physics, physiology, psychiatry, psychology, sociology, and zoology.

The articles are arranged alphabetically by the scientist's name, and almost all of them are accompanied by an illustration, usually a photograph or drawing of the individual under consideration. The format of the articles, which average two thousand words in length, is standard, beginning with a ready-reference listing, including birth and death dates and places, areas of achievement, and a short statement of the scientist's overall contribution. The remainder of the article is divided into four parts. The Early Life section covers the scientist's life up to the point at which his major work in science began. The Life's Work section chronologically follows the figure, relating major events and achievements in the scientist's career. The Summary section constitutes an evaluation of the figure's contribution to or impact on history within his discipline, placing him in context within his field. Citations of published works in text include on first mention the date of first publication and, if the work is foreign, its English translation title and date. The final section is an annotated, evaluative bibliography, which is intended to serve as a starting point for further research. Works are chosen for their accessibility and availability. Articles, therefore, are meant to provide the reader breadth of coverage, ease in obtaining quick information, and recommendations for deeper study. All articles are written and signed by academicians.

Each volume contains a list of contents for that volume as well as a complete list of contents for the set. There are indexes by name and by area of achievement in volume 12.

CONTRIBUTING REVIEWERS

Linda Perry Abrams
Bob Jones University

Stephen R. Addison
University of Central Arkansas

C. D. Alexander
University of Minnesota at Duluth

Arthur L. Alt
College of Great Falls

Michael S. Ameigh
Saint Bonaventure University

Richard J. Amundson
Columbus College

John D. Anderson, Jr.
University of Maryland at College Park

Andrew J. Angyal
Elon College

Stanley Archer
Texas A&M University

James R. Arnold
University of California, San Diego

William Aspray
Charles Babbage Institute
University of Minnesota

Bryan Aubrey
Maharishi International University

Theodore P. Aufdemberge
Concordia College

Lawrence Badash
University of California, Santa Barbara

Richard Badessa
University of Louisville

Brian S. Baigrie
University of Calgary

Dan Barnett
Butte College

Massimo D. Bezoari
Coker College

Robert E. Bieder
Indiana University, Bloomington

Roger E. Bilstein
University of Houston—Clear Lake

Cynthia A. Bily
Adrian College

Julia B. Boken
State University of New York
College at Oneonta

Scott Bouvier
California State University, Los Angeles

David Warren Bowen
Livingston University

Keith Bowen
Southern Oregon State College

Michael R. Bradley
Motlow State Community College

John Braeman
University of Nebraska at Lincoln

Gerhard Brand
California State University, Los Angeles

Jeanie R. Brink
Arizona State University

Celeste Williams Brockington
Independent Scholar

Judit Brody
Independent Scholar

Alan Brown
Livingston University

Robert I. Burns
University of California, Los Angeles

Stephen Burwood
State University of New York at Binghamton

Andrew J. Butrica
Cité des Sciences et de l'Industrie, Paris

Byron D. Cannon
University of Utah, Salt Lake City

Elof Axel Carlson
State University of New York at Stony Brook

W. Bernard Carlson
University of Virginia

P. John Carter
Saint Cloud State University

Dennis Chamberland
Independent Scholar

James T. Chambers
Texas Christian University

David F. Channell
University of Texas at Dallas

Allan D. Charles
University of South Carolina, Union Campus

Deborah Charlie
California State University, Northridge

Victor W. Chen
Chabot College

Eric Christensen
Independent Scholar

Ellen Clark
Independent Scholar

Maureen Connolly
Independent Scholar

Bernard A. Cook
Loyola University, New Orleans

Patricia Cook
Emory University

Albert B. Costa
Duquesne University

James A. Cowan
East Tennessee State University

Annette Daniel
Arkansas College

Ronald W. Davis
Western Michigan University

Frank Day
Clemson University

Charles A. Dranguet, Jr.
Southeastern Louisiana University

William E. Eagan
Moorhead State University

Bruce L. Edwards
Bowling Green State University

Harry J. Eisenman
University of Missouri at Rolla

Michael M. Eisman
Temple University

Robert P. Ellis
Worcester State College

Paul H. Elovitz
Ramapo College of New Jersey

Nancy L. Erickson
Erskine College

Paul F. Erwin
University of Cincinnati

Gary B. Ferngren
Oregon State University

Robert D. Fiala
Concordia College

Donald M. Fiene
University of Tennessee at Knoxville

K. Thomas Finley
State University of New York at Brockport

Robert J. Forman
Saint John's University, New York

Shirley F. Fredricks
Adams State College

C. George Fry
Saint Francis College

Daniel J. Fuller
Kent State University

Keith Garebian
Independent Scholar

Leonardas V. Gerulaitis
Oakland University

Catherine Gilbert
Independent Scholar

Paul E. Gill
Shippensburg University

Joseph A. Goldenberg
Virginia State University

Marvin Goldwert
New York Institute of Technology

Clinton A. Gould
University of Pennsylvania

Karen Gould
University of Texas at Austin

CONTRIBUTING REVIEWERS

Reva Greenburg
Rhode Island College

J. S. Hamilton
Old Dominion University

E. Lynn Harris
University of Illinois

Fred R. van Hartesveldt
Fort Valley State College

Robert M. Hawthorne, Jr.
Unity College

John A. Heitmann
University of Dayton

Julius M. Herz
Temple University

Sally Hibbin
Independent Scholar

Michael Craig Hillmann
University of Texas at Austin

James R. Hofmann
California State University, Fullerton

J. Donald Hughes
University of Denver

Shakuntala Jayaswal
University of New Haven

Reese V. Jenkins
Rutgers University, New Brunswick

Loretta Turner Johnson
Mankato State University

Philip Dwight Jones
Bradley University

J. A. Jungerman
University of California, Davis

Anand Karnad
Boston City Hospital

Robert B. Kebric
University of Louisville

Jeanette Keith
Vanderbilt University

Kenneth F. Kiple
Bowling Green State University

Kenneth F. Kitchell, Jr.
Louisiana State University

Wilbur R. Knorr
Stanford University

Philip E. Koerper
Jacksonville State University

Guha Krish
East Tennessee State University

Paul E. Kuhl
Winston-Salem State University

P. R. Lannert
Independent Scholar

Eugene S. Larson
Los Angeles Pierce College

Daniel B. Levine
University of Arkansas, Fayetteville

James Livingston
Northern Michigan University

Rita E. Loos
Framingham State College

Adele Lubell
Independent Scholar

Reinhart Lutz
University of California, Santa Barbara

C. S. McConnell
University of Calgary

Mark McCulloh
Davidson College

William McGucken
University of Akron

Kerrie L. MacPherson
University of Hong Kong

Paul Madden
Hardin-Simmons University

Philip Magnier
Independent Scholar

Paolo Mancuso
Stanford University

Bill Manikas
Gaston College

William C. Marceau
Saint John Fisher College

Lyndon Marshall
College of Great Falls

Paul Marx
University of New Haven

Elaine Mathiasen
Independent Scholar

Bernard Mergen
George Washington University

Richard D. Miles
Wayne State University

Sara Joan Miles
Wheaton College

Gordon L. Miller
Independent Scholar

Mary-Emily Miller
Salem State College

Peter Monaghan
Independent Scholar

Raymond Lee Muncy
Harding University

Terence R. Murphy
American University

D. Gosselin Nakeeb
Pace University

Nancy J. Nersessian
Princeton University

Brian J. Nichelson
United States Air Force Academy

Steven M. Oberhelman
Texas A&M University

James H. O'Donnell III
Marietta College

Kathleen K. O'Mara
State University of New York
College at Oneonta

James Owen
Purdue University, West Lafayette

Robert J. Paradowski
Rochester Institute of Technology

Harold M. Parker, Jr.
Western State College of Colorado

Judith A. Parsons
Sul Ross State University

William E. Pemberton
University of Wisconsin—La Crosse

Mark Pestana
University of Chicago

John R. Phillips
Purdue University, Calumet

Donald K. Pickens
North Texas State University

Evelyne L. Pickett
University of Nevada at Reno

Ronald L. Pollitt
University of Cincinnati

William S. Pretzer
Henry Ford Museum and Greenfield Village

Edna B. Quinn
Salisbury State University

Sanford Radner
Montclair State College

Thomas Rankin
Independent Scholar

John Ranlett
State University of New York
College at Potsdam

Eugene L. Rasor
Emory and Henry College

Dennis Reinhartz
University of Texas at Arlington

Clark G. Reynolds
Independent Scholar

John S. Rigden
University of Missouri at St. Louis

Joseph F. Rishel
Duquesne University

Francesca Rochberg-Halton
University of Notre Dame

Charles W. Rogers
Southwestern Oklahoma State University

Joseph Rosenblum
University of North Carolina at Greensboro

Marc Rothenberg
Smithsonian Institution

Emanuel D. Rudolph
Ohio State University

Victor Anthony Rudowski
Clemson University

CONTRIBUTING REVIEWERS

Mary Wilson Sage
Duquesne University

Per Schelde
York College

Nancy Schiller
State University of New York at Buffalo

Bernard Schlessinger
Texas Woman's University

June H. Schlessinger
University of North Texas

Robert W. Seidel
Bradbury Science Museum
Los Alamos National Laboratory

Roger Sensenbaugh
Indiana University, Bloomington

David Shayt
Smithsonian Institution

Martha Sherwood-Pike
University of Oregon

R. Baird Shuman
University of Illinois at Urbana-Champaign

Sanford S. Singer
University of Dayton

Carl Singleton
Fort Hays State University

Andrew C. Skinner
Ricks College

Genevieve Slomski
Independent Scholar

Ronald F. Smith
Massachusetts Maritime Academy

Katherine Snipes
Eastern Washington University

Norbert C. Soldon
West Chester University of Pennsylvania

Katherine R. Sopka
Four Corners Analytic Sciences

Kenneth S. Spector
University of Massachusetts, Amherst

Joseph L. Spradley
Wheaton College

David L. Sterling
University of Cincinnati

John Knox Stevens
Indiana University, Bloomington

Paul Stuewe
Independent Scholar

Roger H. Stuewer
University of Minnesota at Minneapolis

Joyce Suellentrop
Kansas Newman College

Patricia E. Sweeney
Independent Scholar

Roy Talbert, Jr.
University of South Carolina
Coastal Carolina College

Alice Taylor
Shorter College

Daniel Taylor
Bethel College

Thomas John Thomson
Limestone College

Greg Tomko-Pavia
Independent Scholar

Ralph Troll
Augustana College

Carole Watterson Troxler
Elon College

William Urban
Monmouth College

George W. Van Devender
Hardin-Simmons University

Abraham Verghese
East Tennessee State University

Charles L. Vigue
University of New Haven

Heinrich von Staden
Yale University

Zuoyue Wang
University of California, Santa Barbara

Brent Waters
University of Redlands

Martha Ellen Webb
University of Nebraska at Lincoln

Michael J. Welsh
Illinois State University

Orren P. Whiddon
Independent Scholar

Robert E. Whipple
Fullerton College

Sherrill Whyte
University of California, Berkeley

Lance Williams
University of Missouri at Rolla

William Van Willis
California State University, Fullerton

David B. Wilson
Iowa State University

John D. Windhausen
Saint Anselm College

George Wise
General Electric Company
Corporate Research and Development

Michael Witkoski
South Carolina House of Representatives

William Ross Woofenden
Swedenborg School of Religion

Frank Wu
University of Wisconsin—Madison

Clifton K. Yearley
State University of New York at Buffalo

Ivan L. Zabilka
Independent Scholar

Ronald Edward Zupko
Marquette University

CONTENTS
VOLUME ONE

COMPLETE CONTENTS

Volume 1

Volume 2

Volume 3

Volume 4

Volume 5

Volume 6

Volume 7

Volume 8

Volume 9

Volume 10

Volume 11

Volume 12

THE GREAT SCIENTISTS

PIETRO D'ABANO

Born: c. 1250; Abano, near Padua, Italy
Died: 1316; Padua, Italy
Areas of Achievement: Medicine and philosophy
Contribution: Pietro founded the Paduan school of medicine, introducing elements of Arabic knowledge into Italy. While a successful professor of medicine, he worked toward a synthesis of medieval, classical, Arabic, and Jewish philosophy.

Early Life

Pietro d'Abano, also known as Peter of Abano, Petrus de Apono, and Petrus Aponensis, was born in the village of Abano near Padua in northern Italy about 1250. Not much is known concerning his family background or early years. His father was a public notary and seems to have been reasonably well-to-do, for Pietro was able to receive an unusually good education. As a youth, he went to Greece and Constantinople, where he gained a mastery of the Greek language; among his early writings are translations of works of Aristotle into Latin. The ability to read the Greek classics in the original was quite unusual in Western Europe before the invading Ottoman Turks began to force Greek scholars to flee westward from the collapsing Byzantine Empire in the mid-fifteenth century.

Upon his return from Constantinople, Pietro attended the University of Paris, perhaps the best of the few institutions of higher learning that existed in late thirteenth century Europe. He studied philosophy, mathematics, and medicine for a number of years and earned a doctorate. Pietro's fame as a scholar and teacher quickly spread, and he became known as "the great Lombard."

Life's Work

In addition to his scientific and philosophical studies, Pietro was very interested in the pseudoscience of astrology. He often included astrological considerations and prayer in his medical prescriptions. Later in his life he was responsible for the inscription of some four hundred astrological symbols on Padua's city hall. His reaching for supernatural forces was probably a reaction to the limited scientific knowledge of the fourteenth century. Pietro himself, for example, asserted firmly that it was impossible to determine the constituent parts of a compound. Thus, without outside help, the medieval scientist was so restricted as to be almost helpless. His astrological interests, however, eventually led to trouble with the Church.

Pietro was more a man of the Middle Ages than of the early Renaissance. His idea of the four elements—earth, water, air, and fire—was typical of medieval understanding of chemistry, but he went further than most medi-

Library of Congress

eval scholars through experimentation and critical translation of classical manuscripts. Pietro was also an eager collector of new information. He left record of an interview with Marco Polo held shortly before the latter returned to Venice in 1295. Pietro inquired about natural phenomena and drugs such as camphor, aloe, and brazil, which were imported from the Orient. He made no mention of magic or other supernatural matters.

Pietro is often called a disciple of the Arabic scholar Avicenna and even more so of Averroës, whose ideas he is supposed to have introduced into Europe. Pietro's ideas about the stages of disease—onset, increase, fullness, and decline—correspond to those of Avicenna, as does his preference for simple, natural medicines. Lynn Thorndike, however, argues quite effectively that the supposed influence of Averroës has no basis in Pietro's writings. Averroës' ideas about chemistry were more sophisticated than those of medieval Europeans such as Pietro, and Thorndike finds no reason to think that Pietro's theological ideas came from the same source. Other writers, however, suggest that Pietro's adoption of a corruption of Averroës' idea of the soul was one of the principal sources of his trouble with the Church.

In addition to numerous translations from Arabic and Greek, Pietro wrote at least ten books. The most famous is the *Conciliator differentiarum philosophorum et praecipue medicorum* (1472; conciliator of the various medical philosophies and practices), in which he attempted to reconcile the teachings of Greek, Arabic, Jewish, and Latin writers in philosophy and medicine. Although done with the usual medieval resort to authority and syllogism, this work contains much original comment and makes clear Pietro's deep commitment to astrology.

Pietro's second major work, *De venenis eorumque remediis* (1473; English translation, 1924), is a description of all important known poisons with descriptions of symptoms and antidotes or treatments. Reportedly done for a pope—possibly John XXII—it too is a mixture of astrology and superstition, but the listing of poisons and symptoms is well done.

Pietro's writings other than translations are *Expositio problematum Aristotelis* (1475; exposition of Aristotelian problems), *Hippocratis de medicorum astrologia libellus Graeco in Latinum* (1476; Hippocratus' astronomical medicine translated from Greek to Latin), *Textus Mesue emendatus Petri Apponi medici in librum* (1505; the text of Mesue amended by Dr. Pietro d'Abano), *Astrolabium planum, in tabulis ascendens, continens qualibet hora atque minuto aequationes domorum coeli, significationes* (1502; clear astronomical tables, containing the heavenly signs for any hour and minute), *Joannis Mesue additio* (1505; additions to John Mesue), *Decisiones physiognomicae* (1548; judging a person's character by physical features), *Geomantia* (1549; *Magical Elements*, 1655), and *De balneis* (1553; on baths). Many of these works were considered authoritative into the sixteenth century.

Although the details are in some dispute, Pietro's return to Padua from Paris seems to have been marked by serious trouble with the Church. Either shortly before or after his arrival in Padua, Pietro was accused of heresy and necromancy. The charges were made through the Dominican Order of friars and were based on reports of a physician named Petrus de Reggio. There are a number of reported accusations, including that he used magic to get all the money he spent returned to him; that he claimed that some biblical miracles had natural explanations; and that he adhered to the rationalistic philosophy of Averroës. Charged with several others, Pietro had to face the Inquisition. Thanks to the intervention of influential patrons—there is one report that Pietro went to Rome and won the support of Pope Boniface VIII—he was exonerated in 1306. In 1314, Pietro was offered the chair of medicine at the new University of Treviso, but he fell ill and died before he could move there. His death was fortuitous in one sense, for in 1315 the charges of heresy were renewed. Posthumously he was condemned and orders were issued for the exhumation and burning of his body. Although most authorities maintain that friends spirited the body away to a new tomb and only an effigy was burned in the public square of Padua, Thomas of Strassburg, Augustinian prior general, claims to have seen the body burned. The distinction seems academic at best.

Thorndike, who has made the most thorough study of Pietro, rejects much of the story of his troubles with the Inquisition. It was, Thorndike argues, constructed of whole cloth in the fifteenth and sixteenth centuries. Pietro may have had one brush with church authorities, but the embellishments about the body being spirited away have no basis in original sources. Thorndike is not even convinced that Pietro died on the traditionally accepted date of 1316 and suggests that he may, in fact, have taught for some years at Treviso after that date. Thorndike's arguments are well marshaled, but they have not been widely adopted by other scholars.

Summary

Pietro was a medieval scientist, but he showed some of the qualities that would mark the Renaissance as well. His critical attitude and experimental approach were signs of the future. The importance he placed on astrology and prayer as elements in medical prescriptions, however, harked back to the past.

Pietro played an important role in the development of Padua and its university into a major intellectual center. Although in the thirteenth century the University of Padua was known mostly for the study of law, by 1500 it could boast of having had many of the major scientists of the Italian Renaissance as professors or students. Pietro founded the Paduan school of medical thought, introducing both classical and Arabic sources. His willingness to question established views and to seek new information rather than depending wholly on authority was important in shaping the growing scholarly tradition of Padua.

Bibliography

Brown, Horace. "*De venenis* of Petrus Abbonus." *Annals of Medical History* 6 (1924): 25-53. A translation of Pietro's work about poisons and their symptoms and treatments, this is the only conveniently available English translation of any of Pietro's writings. It provides a good sample of the mix of superstition and science that marked his approach to medicine.

Castiglioni, Arturo. *A History of Medicine*. New York: Alfred A. Knopf, 1941. Contains a short biographical sketch of Pietro and much useful background information about late medieval medicine and the development of medical studies in Padua.

Hyde, J. K. *Padua in the Age of Dante*. New York: Barnes and Noble Books, 1966. An excellent description of late medieval Padua which provides valuable background information about the milieu in which Pietro worked.

Olschki, Leonardo. "Medical Matters in Marco Polo's Description of the World." In *Essays in the History of Medicine Presented to Professor Arturo Castiglioni on the Occasion of his Seventieth Birth Day*, edited by Henry E. Sigerist. Baltimore: Johns Hopkins University Press, 1944. Contains a discussion of Pietro's interview with Marco Polo showing the former's scientific approach to collecting new data.

Thorndike, Lynn. *A History of Magic and Experimental Science*. Vol. 2. New York: Columbia University Press, 1947. A magisterial work in eight volumes tracing the development of the techniques of modern science. Contains the most complete study of Pietro yet done.

___________. "Peter of Abano: A Medieval Scientist." *Annual Report of the American Historical Association for the Year 1919* 1 (1923): 317-326. Contains a summary of Pietro's life but is focused on historiographical sources. Attempts to show that many common beliefs about Pietro are misconceptions based on secondary sources from the fifteenth and sixteenth centuries.

Fred R. van Hartesveldt

NIELS HENRIK ABEL

Born: August 5, 1802; Finnøy, Norway
Died: April 6, 1829; Froland, Norway
Area of Achievement: Mathematics
Contribution: Abel was instrumental in the evolution of modern mathematics, especially in the field of algebra. Regarded as one of the foremost analysts of his time, he insisted on a rigorous approach to mathematical proof which was critical for the further development of abstract mathematics.

Early Life

Niels Henrik Abel was the second child of Søren Georg Abel, a second-generation Lutheran minister, and Anne Marie Simonsen, a daughter of a successful merchant and shipowner. Soon after his birth in Finnöy, his father was transferred to the parish of Gjerstad, in southeastern Norway, about 250 kilometers from Oslo, where Abel spent his childhood with his five brothers and sisters. Abel was an attractive youth, with light ash-brown hair and blue eyes.

Although his father's earnings were never adequate to provide for the large family, the emphasis on educational stimulation in the Abel household was an important formative influence on the young boy. Although his early education was conducted at home, it was sufficient to allow him to attend the Cathedral School at Oslo when he was thirteen years old. It was there that his talent in mathematics was discovered, although his initial efforts were somewhat unpromising.

The Cathedral School had once been quite good, but many positions had been filled by inexperienced or inadequate teachers because their predecessors had been recruited to join the faculty of the newly formed University of Oslo. Indeed, Abel's first mathematics instructor was dismissed abruptly after beating a student to death. Fortunately, the replacement in that position was Bernt Michael Holmboe, who was the first to recognize Abel's talent and who later edited the first edition of his work. Holmboe also assisted Christopher Hansteen, a professor at the university; this connection would prove valuable to Abel.

When Holmboe first arrived at the school, he noticed Abel's ability in mathematics and suggested that the two of them study some of the contemporary mathematics works together. Abel soon outpaced Holmboe and began developing a general solution for the quintic equation, that is, an equation of the fifth degree ($ax^5 + bx^4 + cx^3 + dx^2 + ex + f = 0$). When Abel believed that the work was complete, Holmboe and Hansteen sensed that no one in Norway, including themselves, could review the work capably. They forwarded the paper to Ferdinand Degen of the Danish Academy, who carefully re-

N. H. Abel

viewed the work. Before publication, Degen helped Abel discover that his solution was flawed, but he steered Abel into the field of elliptic functions, which Degen believed would be more fruitful.

At about this time, Abel discovered that several of his predecessors, particularly Leonhard Euler and Joseph-Louis Lagrange, had not completed the reasoning required to prove some of their work. Abel diligently supplied rigorous proofs where they were missing; a noted case is his proof of the general binomial theorem, which had been stated previously in part by Sir Isaac Newton and Euler. The mathematics community later was to find his meticulous treatment of the works he studied invaluable. Unfortunately for his personal life and his financial situation, Abel's father, who had served two terms in the *Storting* (congress), was impeached and disgraced. His father died in 1829, leaving his family in even more desperate financial straits than ever before.

Life's Work

The nineteen-year-old Abel entered the University of Oslo in 1821. While this entering age would not normally denote a prodigy, the fact that the university granted him a free room and that several professors donated funds for his support does. Abel completed the preliminary requirements for a degree in a single year. He was then free to study mathematics on his own, as he had no peers among the faculty. He developed a love for the theater at this time, which lasted throughout his short life. A modest person, he made many lasting friendships.

In addition to studying all available work, he began writing papers, the first of which were published in the journal *Magazin for Naturvidenskaberne* begun by Hansteen. In 1823, Abel's first important paper, "Opläsning afet Par Opgaver ved bjoelp af bestemte Integraler" ("Solution of Some Problems by Means of Definite Integrals"), was published, containing the first published solutions of integral equations. During 1822 and 1823, he also developed a longer paper discussing the integration of functions. This work is recognized as very significant in the evolution of that field of study.

At this time, Abel's work was largely ignored by the international mathematics community because Abel was from Norway and wrote in Norwegian, and the focal point of the mathematics community of the day was Paris, with the language of the learned being French. By applying himself diligently, Abel learned French and began to publish work in that language. The quintic equation still held his attention, and, as he thought of possibilities for its solution, he also considered that there might be no solution that could be found for all such equations. In time, he was able to prove this result. Yet still the mathematicians whose approval he desired so fervently, those in Paris, ignored his work.

He began to press for the opportunity to go to Paris, but penniless as he

was he was forced to rely on grants. After his first application, it was decided that he needed to study more foreign languages before going abroad. Although it meant delaying his dream for nearly two years, Abel applied himself to learning various languages. Meanwhile, he became engaged to Christine (Krelly) Kemp before he finally received a royal grant to travel abroad in 1825.

This trip was unsuccessful in many ways. When he arrived at Copenhagen, he discovered that Degen had died. Instead of going on to Paris, Abel decided to go to Berlin because several of his friends were there. The time in Berlin was invaluable, for he met and befriended August Leopold Crelle, who became his strongest supporter and mentor. When Abel met him, Crelle was preparing to begin publication of a new journal, *Journal für die reine und angewandte Mathematik*. Crelle was so taken by Abel's ability that much of the first few issues was devoted to Abel's work in an attempt to win recognition for the young mathematician.

For a variety of reasons, Abel did not proceed to Paris until the spring of 1826. By this time, he had spent most of his grant and was physically tired, and the Parisian mathematicians he had hoped to convince were nearly all on holiday. Yet his masterwork, *Mémoire sur une propriété générale d'une classe très-étendue de fonctions transcendantes* (memoir on a general property of a very extensive class of transcendental functions), was presented to the Academy of Sciences on October 30, 1826. The paper was left in the keeping of Augustin-Louis Cauchy, a prominent mathematician, and Cauchy and Adrien-Marie Legendre were to be the referees. Whether the paper was illegible, as Cauchy claimed, or was misplaced, as most historians believe, no judgment was issued until after Abel's death.

Abel felt a great sense of failure, for many young mathematicians had been established by recognition from the academy. He returned first to Berlin and finally to Oslo in May, 1827. His prospects were bleak: He had contracted tuberculosis, there was no prospect for a mathematical position in Norway, and he was in debt. Abel began tutoring and lecturing at the university on a substitute basis in order to support himself.

Another young mathematician, Carl Gustav Jacob Jacobi, soon began publishing work in Abel's foremost field, the theory of elliptic functions and integrals. The rivalry created between them dominated the rest of Abel's life. He worked furiously to prove his ideas, and his efforts were spurred by his correspondence with Legendre. As he finally began to be recognized in Europe, many mathematicians, led by Crelle, attempted to secure a patronage for him. He succumbed, however, to tuberculosis on April 6, 1829, two days before Crelle wrote to inform him that such financial support had been found. In June, 1830, he and Jacobi were awarded the Grand Prix of the French Academy of Sciences for their work in elliptic integrals. Abel's original manuscript was found and finally published in 1841.

Summary

Although Niels Henrik Abel's life was short and his work was unrecognized for most of his life, he has exercised a great influence on modern mathematics. His primary work with elliptic functions and integrals led to interest in what became one of the great research topics of his century. Without his preliminary findings, many of the developments in mathematics and, consequently, science, may not have been made. One example of this is his theory of elliptic functions, much of which was developed very quickly during his race with Jacobi. In addition, his proof that there is no general solution to the quintic equation is quite important, as are his other findings in equation theory.

His theory of solutions using definite integrals, including what is now called Abel's theorem, is also widely used in engineering and the physical sciences and provided a foundation for the later work of others. Abelian (commutative) groups, Abelian functions, and Abelian equations are but three of the ideas which commonly carry his name. Given Abel's short life span and his living in Norway, a definite academic backwater at the time, his prolific achievements are amazing.

Abel is also significant because his writing and mathematical styles, which were easily comprehended, made his discoveries available to his contemporaries and successors. Abel's insistence that ideas should be demonstrated in such a way that the conclusions would be supported by clear and easily comprehended arguments, that is, proved rigorously, is the cornerstone of modern mathematics. It is in this regard that Abel is most often remembered.

Bibliography

Abel, Niels Henrik. "From a Memoir on Algebraic Equations, Proving the Impossibility of a Solution of the General Equation of the Fifth Degree." In *Classics of Mathematics*, edited by Ronald Calinger. Oak Park, Ill.: Moore, 1982. This extract of Abel's paper on the general quintic equation demonstrates Abel's style. Although it is too technical for the casual reader, it is of interest to mathematicians. The excerpt is preceded by a brief biography. This work also demonstrates how Abel fits into the overall development of mathematics.

Bell, Eric T. "Genius and Poverty: Abel." In *Men of Mathematics*. New York: Simon & Schuster, 1937. This book is a compilation of brief biographies of the most famous mathematicians throughout recorded history. The emphasis is more on the subject's life than the mathematics produced.

Boyer, Carl B. *A History of Mathematics*. New York: John Wiley & Sons, 1968. This general history of mathematics will aid the reader in placing Abel within the general development of mathematics.

Kline, Morris. *Mathematical Thought from Ancient to Modern Times*. New York: Oxford University Press, 1972. Kline includes both a brief biography of Abel and discussions of his most important work in this history of mathematics.

Ore, Øystein. *Niels Henrik Abel: Mathematician Extraordinary.* Minneapolis: University of Minnesota Press, 1957. This standard English-language biography gives a detailed account of Abel's life without requiring specialized knowledge of mathematics.

Celeste Williams Brockington

ABUL WEFA

Born: June 10, 940; either Buzshan, Khorasan Province, or Buzadhan, Kuhistan Province, Iran
Died: July 1, 998; Baghdad
Areas of Achievement: Mathematics and astronomy
Contribution: Abul Wefa played a major role in the development of sines and cosines as they apply to the field of trigonometry. These he used to correct astronomical calculations carried forward from classical into Islamic times.

Early Life

Born in 940, during the reign of the 'Abbasid caliph al-Mutaqqi, Abul Wefa lived during a period of extraordinary cultural and intellectual productivity. His own fields of accomplishment, mathematics and astronomy, were already widely recognized as essential elements of high Islamic civilization. Very little seems to be known about Abul Wefa's early life. Apparently, his early education in mathematics occurred under the tutelage of two uncles, one of whom (Abu Amr al-Mughazili) had received formal training from the famous geometricians Abu Yahya Al-Marwazi and Abu'l Ala ibn Karnib.

Whatever the possible source of patronage for the young man's further education may have been, his decision to move to Baghdad at the age of nineteen (in 959) greatly benefited the 'Abbasid court. Baghdad at this time was politically troubled, following the seizure of *de facto* control by a military clique headed by the Persian Buyid emirs; thereafter, the Buyids dominated the house of the caliphs until their fall from power in 1055. The Buyids were inclined to favor talented Persians who were drawn toward scholarly circles in the center of the empire. It is reported, for example, that it was Abul Wefa, himself then forty years of age and well established (circa 980), who introduced the Persian scholar and philosopher Abu Hayyan al-Tawhidi into the Baghdad entourage of the vizier Ibn Sa'dan. Abu Hayyan soon became famous under the vizier's patronage, composing a major work, *al-Imta' wa'l mu'anasa* (a collection of notes drawn from philosophical and literary "salon" meetings), under a dedication to Ibn Sa'dan.

Patronage for Abul Wefa's work in courtly circles, however, must have come from a different milieu, that of the so-called Baghdad School. This scientific assembly flourished in the 'Abbasid capital in the last century before its conquest by the Seljuk Turks in 1055. According to some historians, patronage for the natural sciences in particular came precisely during the period in which Abul Wefa passed into the main stages of his scholarly career. The Buyid emir Adud al-Dawlah (978-983) had nurtured an interest in astronomy through his own studies. He passed this interest on to his son,

Saraf al-Dawlah, who built an observatory next to his palace and called scholars from all regions of the empire to glorify the reputation of his reign by carrying out scientific experiments. Abul Wefa was among this group.

Life's Work

The environment for learning in the Baghdad School, with its circle of eminent Islamic scientists, may explain how the young Persian scholar mastered so many technical fields in such a limited period of time. Beyond mere speculation regarding Abul Wefa's early personal contacts, however, one must consider the importance of translation work in the Baghdad School. Abul Wefa himself translated the work of the Greek algebraist Diophantus (fl. c. A.D. 250), who had explored the field of indeterminate algebraic equations. Abul Wefa was also known for his studies of, and commentaries on, Euclid. There are, however, no surviving texts to indicate what use he made of the work of these two forerunners from the classical pre-Islamic period.

By contrast, Abul Wefa's attention to the work of the second century Greek astronomer Ptolemy not only contributed to the preservation and transmission to the medieval West of the classical knowledge contained in Ptolemy's *Mathēmatikē suntaxis* (c. A.D. 150; *Almagest*) but also earned for him an original and lasting reputation as an Islamic mathematician. The *Almagest* examined the field of trigonometry, which proposed mathematical relationships in terms of the angles and sides of right triangles. This called for the development of sines, or systematic relationships defined in a right triangle working from one of the acute angles, symbolically represented as A. Modern trigonometry expresses this relationship as $\sin A = a/c$, or $\sin A$ is equal to the ratio of the length of the side opposite that angle (a) to the length of the hypotenuse (c).

Ptolemy, in pioneering the field of spherical trigonometry, had laid down an approximate method for calculating sines (which he described as "chords"). Abul Wefa, however, drew on his studies of Indian precedents in the field of trigonometry that were unknown to Ptolemy, as well as models provided by Abul Wefa's predecessor al-Battani (858-929), to perfect Ptolemy's chords. This was done by applying algebraic, instead of geometric, methods of systematizing the sines. In particular, Abul Wefa's development of the "half-chord" made it possible to achieve much more precise measurements that would eventually be used in surveying and navigation. The most immediate application of his tables of sines, however, was in the field of astronomy.

One of Abul Wefa's contributions which left a legacy that lasted for many centuries involved the study of evection, or irregularity, in the longitude of the moon. Later European commentators, including Louis Pierre E. A. Sédillot in the nineteenth century, looked at the Islamic astronomer's work and concluded that he, not Tycho Brahe (1546-1601), had been the first sci-

entist to posit the theory of the "third inequality of the moon." Although this theory was later proved to be erroneous, the debate at least drew attention to the importance of Abul Wefa's originality in the field.

Abul Wefa himself compiled, in addition to his well-known tables of sines, a book of astronomical tables entitled *Zij al-wadih* (that which is clear). Like his earlier work on sines, this text is not extant in the original. Scholars tend to agree, however, that certain anonymous manuscripts preserved in European libraries, such as the *Zij al-shamil*, are taken from Abul Wefa's work.

Works that have survived and that have been at least partially translated include a book of arithmetic entitled *Kitab fi ma yahtaj ilayh al-kuttab wa l-'ummal min 'ilm al-hisab* (961-976; book on what is necessary from the science—of arithmetic for scribes and businessmen), the *Kitab fi ma yahtaj ilayh al-sani 'min al-a'mal al-handasiyha* (after 990; book on what is necessary from geometric construction for the artisan), and a book entitled *Kitab al-kamil* (translated by Carra de Vaux in the *Journal Asiatique* of 1892). It is thought that Abul Wefa may have still been in Baghdad at the time of his death in 998.

Summary

Study of the Islamic cultural milieu in which Abul Wefa lived suggests a high level of syncretic interaction between ethnic subjects of the Baghdad Caliphate—Arab, Persian, Greek, or other minorities. Abul Wefa's own career seems also to provide an example of a syncretic social hierarchy. Scientists and intellectual figures, it seems, had no reason to doubt that their accomplishments would be appreciated and supported by a ruling military elite whose social status was obviously determined by very different criteria. In this rather cosmopolitan period in Islamic history, there was room not only for scholars of diverse national origins at the caliph's court but also for representatives of different disciplines, secular and religious, to live side by side in a community that was truly representative of a world civilization. One can only understand the flourishing in Islam of such different disciplines (and the pure sciences in particular), however, if attention is given to the multiplicity of pre-Islamic sources that contributed both to the Baghdad Caliphate itself and to the highly developed cultural institutions that it supported.

Bibliography

Bell, Eric T. *The Development of Mathematics*. New York: McGraw-Hill Book Co., 1945. Begins with a historical review of the field of mathematics from the first known texts through successive stages of discoveries, ending at mid-point in the twentieth century. The chapter which is of most interest to students of Islamic science is entitled "Detour Through India, Arabia, and Spain, 400-1300." This title underscores the importance of the medieval period of Oriental history for the conservation of classical Western

sources which only returned to Europe via the Islamic core zone, from eastern Iran to Spain.

Cajori, Florian. *A History of Mathematics*. New York: Macmillan, 1931. This rather dated work has several important characteristics which merit mention. It covers not only standard non-Western mathematical traditions (Hindu and Islamic) but also traditions from little-studied areas such as Mayan Central America and Japan. Cajori also manages to give detailed information on individual mathematicians' original findings while keeping information on a sufficiently comprehensible level for the layman.

Kennedy, E. S., ed. *Studies in the Islamic Exact Sciences*. Beirut, Lebanon: American University of Beirut Press, 1983. Provides a rather technical treatment of several scientific disciplines that flourished in early Islamic times, including the development, through trigonometry, of accurate astronomical calculations. A specific elaboration of Abul Wefa's work is included in this collection of essays, but the prospective reader should be aware that a substantial background in mathematics will be necessary to follow stage-by-stage explanations.

Nasr, Seyyed Hossein. *Islamic Science: An Illustrated Survey*. London: World of Islam Festival, 1976. A carefully researched photographic record of the tools of Islamic science. Textual treatment of historical figures such as Abul Wefa is more limited than in Nasr's *Science and Civilization in Islam*. The choice of illustrations, however, particularly from Islamic astronomy, is so rich that the field itself becomes a much more coherent entity.

___________. *Science and Civilization in Islam*. Cambridge, Mass.: Harvard University Press, 1968. Because this work deals with the subject of science in Islamic civilization only, it can take time to explore individual contributions at some length.

Byron D. Cannon

ALFRED ADLER

Born: February 7, 1870; Penzing, Austria
Died: May 28, 1937; Aberdeen, Scotland
Areas of Achievement: Medicine and social science
Contribution: Adler, the founder of individual psychology, introduced such fundamental mental-health concepts as "inferiority feeling," "life-style," "striving for superiority," and "social interest." The first to occupy a chair of medical psychology in the United States, Adler pioneered the use of psychiatry in both social work and early childhood education.

Early Life

Alfred Adler was born on February 7, 1870, in Penzing, Austria, a suburb of Vienna, the second of seven children of Leopold Adler, a Jewish Hungarian grain merchant from the Burgenland, and his wife, a native of Moravia. Though reared on a farm, Adler was exposed to the rich cultural life of Vienna's golden age. The death of a younger brother and his own bout with pneumonia at the age of five caused Adler to resolve to study medicine. He received his medical degree in 1895 from the University of Vienna. Much later, Adler would be awarded his Ph.D. from the Long Island College of Medicine in New York. In 1895, Adler married Raissa Timofejewna Epstein, a Moscow-born student. Together they had three daughters and a son. Two of his children, Kurt and Alexandra, later took up the practice of psychiatry. By 1897, Adler was practicing general medicine in Vienna, specializing in ophthalmology. His zeal for reform was indicated in articles in various socialist newspapers.

Though Adler's first professional monograph had been a study of the health of tailors, by 1900 he had become interested in neurology and in psychopathological symptoms. His review in 1902 of Sigmund Freud's book on dream interpretation led to an invitation to join the Vienna Psychoanalytic Society. Though closely associated with Freud (they attended the first International Congress on Psychoanalysis together in 1908), Adler insisted that he was neither Freud's disciple nor his student. This fact was revealed in 1907 in his *Studie über Minderwertigkeit von Organen* (*Study of Organ Inferiority and Its Psychical Compensation*, 1917). In 1911, Adler and nine others resigned from Freud's circle to found the Society for Free Psychoanalysis. Freud then launched what has been called an "almost scurrilous attack" on Adler. For his part, Adler acknowledged his respect for Freud but explained his major intellectual disagreements with him. Adler denied the dominance of the biological over the psychological in human behavior, refusing to see sex as the primary determinant of personality. Adler stressed freedom, not determinism, in conduct, believing that Freud compared humans to animals or machines, forgetting to emphasize what makes them

unique, namely, concepts and values. Adler resolved to champion a holistic, humanistic psychology. By 1912, his *Über den nervösen Charakter* (*The Neurotic Constitution*, 1917) indicated the directions being taken by Adlerian or individual psychology.

During World War I, Adler served in the Austro-Hungarian army as a military doctor on the Russian front at Kraków and Brunn. Returning from three years in the war, Adler established what was probably the world's first child-guidance clinic in Vienna in 1919. Soon thirty such centers were operating in Vienna, Munich, and Berlin. Adler emerged as the first psychiatrist to apply mental hygiene in the schools, lecturing meanwhile at the Pedagogical Institute. A pathfinder of family therapy or community psychiatry, Adler involved students, teachers, and parents in treatment. Innovative counseling was done before a restricted audience as a teaching device. By 1926, Adler was much in demand as a lecturer in Europe and North America, and his work was commanding wide recognition.

Life's Work

Adler's life's work was focused on four areas. Adler was preeminently an educator. In 1926, he became a visiting professor at Columbia University, and in 1932 he became the United States' first professor of medical psychology, teaching at the Long Island College of Medicine in New York. By then his visits to Vienna were seasonal and occasional, terminating after the rise of Fascism in Austria and Germany and the Nazi suppression of his clinics. Adler's lectures were copied and published as *Menschenkenntnis* (1927; *Understanding Human Nature*, 1918), a text that is still a classic.

Second, Adler was widely read as an author. Increasingly his works were directed toward the general public, such as *What Life Should Mean to You* (1931) and *Der Sinn des Lebens* (1933; *Social Interest: A Challenge to Mankind*, 1939). Other volumes included *The Case of Miss R* (1929), *Problems of Neurosis* (1929), *The Case of Miss A* (1931), and *The Pattern of Life* (1930). After his death, Adler's papers were edited by Heinz L. and Rowena R. Ansbacher as *Superiority and Social Interest* (1964) and *The Individual Psychology of Alfred Adler* (1956).

Third, Adler was much sought as a therapist. For Adler, the psychiatrist did not treat mental disease. Rather, he discovered the error in the patient's way of life and then led him toward greater maturity. Therapy was a kind of teaching, with the emphasis on health, not sickness, and on the client's total network of relationships. Adler wanted to know the patient not simply "in depth but in context." The therapist was to be an enabler, helping the patient "see the power of self-determination" and "command the courage" to alter his entire world and his interpretation of it. In analysis, Adler relied on such diagnostic tools as dream interpretation, the meaning of early childhood recollections, and the role of birth order. Not only was therapy social as well as personal, but also it was to be preventative as well as restorative. Adler established clinics to help avoid such life failures as neurosis and psychosis. Adler was one of the first psychiatrists to apply his therapeutic techniques to the treatment of criminals, to the practice of social work, and to the education of American children.

Finally, Adler was in demand as a lecturer. The disarming gentleness that won for him acceptance from patients made him a winsome communicator to audiences. Soon as facile in English as his native German, Adler, a tenor, spoke slowly with occasional silences, pauses that were said to add to the profundity of his remarks. His was a soft voice, but one that was conciliatory and persuading in tone. His piercing eyes and friendly manner evoked a warm response. Though described as stocky and pudgy, Adler conveyed a feeling of intensity and energy with his swift movements and quickness of thought. His broad interests, cinema, cafés, music (he had a fine singing voice), drama, and hiking, established many points of contact with his auditors. It was while on a lecture tour that Adler died at age sixty-seven of a heart attack on Union Street, Aberdeen, Scotland, on May 28, 1937. His daughter, Alexandra, then a research fellow in neurology, completed the tour. Adler's teaching was institutionalized by a series of five international congresses he directed between 1922 and 1930 and since his death by the International Association of Individual Psychology.

Adler believed that the principal human motive was a striving for perfection. He argued in 1907 in *Study of Organ Inferiority and Its Psychical Compensation* that physical disability or inadequacy in the child may result in psychical compensation. Overcompensation can occur. Ludwig van Beethoven, who was losing his hearing, became a master musician. Demosthenes, a stutterer, became a compelling orator. Compensation, however, can produce not only genius but also neurotic and psychotic adaptations to life. In *The Neurotic Constitution*, Adler admitted that inferiority feeling was a condition common to all children. Children respond with an aggression drive (or, later, a striving for superiority). Adler spoke of a masculine protest (found in both males and females), which is any "attempt to overcome socially conditioned feelings of weakness" (such weaknesses being perceived as feminine).

Behavior, Adler taught, is goal oriented. For that reason, his individual psychology is teleological, not causal, as was Freud's. Adler concentrated on the consequences as much as the antecedents of actions. By the age of four or five, Adler insisted, the child has set goals for himself. These goals grow out of the self-image the child has evolved, as well as his opinion of the world. The self is a product not only of objective or external factors, such as birth order, but also of subjective or internal factors, such as interpretation and opinion. A person's creative power resides in "the ability to choose between various ways of reacting to a situation." As a person seeks maturity and wholeness, he selects goals that promise fulfillment and the means by which to attain them. A life-style becomes apparent.

Life, for Adler, consisted in meeting three main problems or fulfilling three main tasks which are "inseparably tied up with the logic of man's communal life." These tasks are occupational, associational, and sexual. A choice of work or vocation reveals the primary influences present in the child before the age of thirteen. Association with others, the development of a significant and healthy system of interpersonal relationships, is crucial. Love and marriage, or sex, is the most important of those associations, for from this relationship comes the next generation.

Failures in life, that is, neurotics (mildly dysfunctional) and psychotics (severely dysfunctional), are those who do not develop social interest. Self-bound, they are crippled with intense inferiority feelings and become obsessed with themselves. Withdrawal from life may result because of a belief that one is unable to compete. Another unhealthy adaptation is the evolving of a superiority that is useful only to themselves. Normality or health for Adler meant moving toward constructive social interest, where the person functions creatively for the welfare of all.

Adler's wide range of activities and his inclusive and practical teachings caused him to become a major new influence in psychiatry in the years following World War I. That impact has been a constant through the subsequent decades.

Summary

Through a creative career on two continents as an educator, author, therapist, and lecturer, Alfred Adler indicated new directions for the infant science of psychiatry. A contemporary of such physicians of the mind as Sigmund Freud and Carl Gustav Jung in Europe and William James in the United States, Adler became one of the founders of the science of mental health. A persuasive and popular communicator, Adler was able to involve the general public in the application of the findings of psychiatry. As a result, what once had been seen as an arcane field provided conversation for cocktail parties. Capitalizing on this widespread public interest, Adler pioneered the application of mental-health techniques to pedagogy, child psychology, school reform, and the teaching and training of an entire generation of educators. Social work in the United States is also greatly indebted to the insights of Adler. Yet it is in the field of psychotherapy that he has had his most lasting influence. Subsequent practitioners of the art of healing the mind, as diverse as Karen Horney, Harry Stack Sullivan, Franz Alexander, and Ian Suttie, have been assisted by the teachings of Adler. Alfred Adler remains one of the giants of medicine and psychiatry and of the creative thought of the twentieth century.

Bibliography

Adler, Alfred. *The Individual Psychology of Alfred Adler*. Edited by Heinz L. Ansbacher and Rowena R. Ansbacher. New York: Grove Press, 1956. This is perhaps the best single anthology of materials by Adler, culled from lectures by two of his disciples. The extracts are accompanied by a complete bibliography and critical annotations of the essays.

Bottome, Phyllis. *Alfred Adler: Apostle of Freedom*. New York: G. P. Putnam's Sons, 1939. 3d ed. London: Faber & Faber, 1957. The author's husband was Adler's secretary. For that reason, the information offered in this 315-page biography rests on eyewitness observation and access to primary papers. Bottome believed Adler to be "at once the easiest of men to know and the most difficult, the frankest and the most subtle, the most conciliatory and the most ruthless."

Dreikurs, Rudolf. *Fundamentals of Adlerian Psychology.* New York: Greenberg, 1950. This concise study initially appeared in 1933. Originally written in German, it dates from the decade of Adler's death and reflects his later thinking. It should be supplemented by more recent works.

Orgler, Hertha. *Alfred Adler, the Man and His Work: Triumph over the Inferiority Complex*. 3d rev. ed. London: G. W. Daniel Co., 1963. This classic study, first published in 1939, is a must for beginning research. Drawing on both contemporary and second-generation opinion of Adler and individual psychology, Orgler's book attempts to view the subject in the light of his own growth toward wholeness.

Rallner, Joseph. *Alfred Adler.* Translated by Harry Zohn. New York: Frederick Ungar, 1983. This work by a German scholar is concise yet comprehensive in its treatment.

C. George Fry

LOUIS AGASSIZ

Born: May 28, 1807; Motier-en-Vuly, Switzerland
Died: December 14, 1873; Cambridge, Massachusetts
Areas of Achievement: Natural history and education
Contribution: Agassiz created an awareness of the importance of the study of natural history in the United States with his founding of the Museum of Comparative Zoology at Harvard University. He was an early pioneer in making scientific studies an integral part of the curriculum at American colleges and universities.

Early Life

Jean Louis Rodolphe Agassiz was born May 28, 1807, in Motier-en-Vuly, Canton Fribourg, Switzerland. The son of a Protestant clergyman, Agassiz was one of four children. At the age of ten, Agassiz was sent to school at Bienne, where he spent much of his time observing freshwater fish, which fascinated him. In 1822, he entered the Academy of Lausanne. Upon graduation, out of deference to his parents, he enrolled in the school of medicine at the University of Zurich. After two years of studies in medicine, he enrolled in the University of Heidelberg, where he developed a special interest in natural history. The following year, he transferred to the University of Munich to study under Ignaz von Döllinger, a pioneer embryologist whom Agassiz credited as the source of his scientific training.

In 1829, he received a doctorate in philosophy at Erlanger and returned to Munich to complete his studies in medicine. The following year, he received a doctorate in medicine and thereafter never examined a patient; his mind was set on pursuing studies in ichthyology, paleontology, and glacial geology.

While Agassiz was enrolled in Munich, Lorenz Oken, one of his professors, presented a paper on Agassiz's discovery of a new species of carp. In 1829, Agassiz published his first book on this species of Brazilian fish based on his study of a collection of specimens from the Amazon brought to Munich in 1821 by J. B. Spix and K. F. Philip von Martius. The book was written with such beauty and clarity that it was soon evident that Agassiz would become not only a man of science but also a man of letters.

Agassiz married Cecile Braun, sister of the eminent botanist Alexander Braun. There were three children born to the union, a son and two daughters. Cecile was a natural history artist whose drawings of fossil and freshwater fish forms appeared in several of Agassiz's books. She died of tuberculosis in 1848.

Agassiz was a large, robust man, slightly above medium height, who had keen brown eyes which could light up with enthusiasm. He had chestnut brown hair that gradually thinned with age but retained its color into his declining years.

Library of Congress

Life's Work

The professional life of Agassiz is clearly divided into two chapters: his work as a research scientist in Europe, in the course of which he made significant advances in the fields of ichthyology and glacial geology, and his teaching career in the United States, during which he dedicated himself to making science an integral and respected part of the curriculum of higher education in his adopted country.

Upon completion of his formal schooling, Agassiz went to Paris to continue his studies in medicine. While there, he spent much of his time at the museum of natural history at the Jardin des Plantes, where he met Georges Cuvier, the master of comparative anatomy. The aging Cuvier willingly turned over much of his unfinished work to the young naturalist to complete. Agassiz also met the naturalist Friedrich Humbolt, who in 1832 secured for him an appointment as professor in natural history at the University of Neuchâtel.

While at Neuchâtel, Agassiz formed a natural history society and took scientists on excursions into the Alps to study and observe flora and fauna. Agassiz turned Neuchâtel into a research center, and over the course of fifteen years he published more than two hundred works, including twenty substantial volumes illustrated with more than two thousand plates. Before Agassiz began his research, only eight generic types of fossil fish had been named in formal publications. Agassiz identified 340 new genera, many of them in his books *History of the Fresh Water Fishes of Central Europe* (1839-1842) and *Monograph on the Fossil Fishes of the Old Red or Devonian of the British Isles and Russia* (1844-1845).

While at Neuchâtel, Agassiz's attention was drawn to the nearby glacier of the great median moraine of the lower Aar valley, and this sent his scientific investigations in a new direction, that of glacial geology. He concluded from his observations that gravity controls glacial movements and that glaciers travel faster in the middle and at the surface, disproving the commonly held theory that glaciers are pushed along by water freezing underneath. He published his findings in *Études sur les glaciers* (1840; studies on glaciers) and *Systèmes glaciaires* (1846; glacial systems). Agassiz came to accept Karl Schimper's "ice age" thesis and added that Europe had been subjected once to a period of extreme cold from the North Pole to the Mediterranean and Caspian seas in a widespread Pleistocene ice age. He studied earth surfaces all over Europe and concluded that drift material and polished and striated boulders gave evidence of earlier glacial movements.

A gift from the King of Prussia in 1846 enabled Agassiz to pursue his work in the United States. Sir Charles Lyell had arranged for him to participate in a course of lectures at the Lowell Institute in Boston. Agassiz's life took another turn. His intense research gave way to teaching and campaigning on behalf of natural history as a legitimate academic endeavor.

Agassiz continued to write of his discoveries with verbal precision and lucid description. He could devote fifty pages of unmatched prose describing the interior of an egg. He set about to produce a twelve-volume series entitled *Contributions to the Natural History of the United States*. More than twenty-five hundred advance subscriptions were taken, but only four volumes were ever produced (1857-1862). These four volumes represented a triumph of thought and scholarship and contributed to the nature-consciousness of the American public.

In 1848, Agassiz accepted the chair of natural history of the new Lawrence Scientific School at Harvard University, and the same year he published his popular *Principles of Zoology*. When he visited Washington, D.C., he was disappointed to find so little scientific activity in the nation's capital. At the time, the Smithsonian Institution had not begun to function. Agassiz was later made a member of the Smithsonian Board of Regents, and the institution's natural history division was developed.

In 1850, Agassiz married Elizabeth Cary, and the following year he accepted a teaching appointment at the Medical College of Charleston, South Carolina. After two years, he resigned because he found the climate unsuitable and returned to Harvard. He and his wife opened a school for young women in Cambridge which became the precursor of Radcliffe College.

Agassiz was quite disappointed with Harvard's science department and claimed that the chemistry laboratory at Cambridge High School was better equipped; he often did his work there. In 1859, Agassiz founded the Museum of Comparative Zoology at Harvard and helped to create a new era in American higher education. He emphasized advanced and original works as factors in mental training and stressed the direct, hands-on study of nature. Ralph Waldo Emerson complained that something ought to be done to check this rush toward natural history at Harvard. Agassiz countered that the rest of the curriculum should be brought up to the standards he had set for the zoology laboratories. Agassiz found a kindred soul in Henry David Thoreau and often visited Walden Pond. At a dinner hosted by Emerson, Thoreau and Agassiz once talked of mating turtles, to the disgust of Emerson. From Walden, Thoreau sent Agassiz varieties of fish, turtles, and snakes, and was paid handsomely for them.

The same year that Agassiz opened the museum at Harvard, Charles Darwin published his *On the Origin of Species by Means of Natural Selection* (1859). The theory of evolution did not begin with Darwin, and Agassiz was thoroughly acquainted with the works of Georges-Louis Leclerc Buffon, Jean Baptiste de Monet de Lamarck, Charles Darwin's own grandfather, Erasmus Darwin, and their ideas of the gradual, continuous progress of species which contributed to the theory of evolution. Also, much of the knowledge of embryology which is integral to Darwin's theory was originally discovered by Agassiz. Agassiz once admitted that he had been on the verge of anticipating Darwinism when he found that the highest fishes were those that came first, and therefore he rejected the theory. Sharks, one of the most primitive species, had the largest brains and the most specialized teeth and muscular systems. Two years before Darwin's theory was published, Agassiz wrote "An Essay on Classification," in which he asserted that the plan of creation was the "free conception" of an all-powerful intelligence in accordance with a predetermined pattern for each of the species, which, he argued, were destined to remain changeless.

Agassiz became Darwin's most formidable opponent in the United States. His studies of fossils led him to conclude that the changes which animals undergo during their embryonic growth coincide with the order of succession of the fossils of the same type in past geological ages. He believed that all species had been immutable since their creation. From time to time, the Creator may have annihilated old species and created new ones. His exhibits at the Harvard museum were intended to reflect the permanence of the species.

Agassiz regarded himself as the "librarian of the works of God," but he was not a theologian and gave no support to those ministers who parroted his responses to Darwin. He claimed that in Europe he was accused of deriving his scientific ideas from the Church and in the United States he was regarded as an infidel because he would not let churchmen pat him on the head. Agassiz believed that there was a creator and even went so far as to posit a multiple creation theory. He claimed that blacks were created separately and were a different species from whites, an argument which gave great comfort to the defenders of slavery in the South.

Only a few American scientists, such as his Harvard colleague Asa Gray, dared to take open issue with the erudite and popular Agassiz before his death. Gray argued that the species had originated in a single creative act and that their variations were the result of causes such as climate, geographical isolation, and the phenomena described by the same glacial theory that Agassiz had done so much to establish.

Agassiz became an American citizen in 1861 and continued his opposition to Darwinism. He fought a losing battle for fifteen years with the Darwinists and went to his grave denying the reality of evolution. His last article, published posthumously in the *Atlantic Monthly* (1874), was entitled "Evolution and the Permanence of Type."

Agassiz was appointed a visiting professor at Cornell in 1868, but the following year he suffered a stroke. Although this slowed him considerably, he continued his strenuous schedule of speaking and writing. In 1872, he sailed on board a coastal survey ship from Boston around the horn to San Francisco. The trip was disappointing, since Agassiz was unable to make the scientific progress he had hoped on the voyage. In 1873, John Anderson of New York deeded the island of Penikese in Buzzards Bay off the coast of Massachusetts and gave fifty thousand dollars to help Agassiz create a summer school for science teachers. The Anderson School of Natural History became the forerunner of the Woods Hole Biological Institute.

Summary

Louis Agassiz was the man who made America nature-conscious. He was a major figure in American nineteenth century culture, in the fields of both literature and science. He assumed that the organization of nature was everyone's concern and that each community should collect and identify the elements of its own zoology and botany.

Agassiz would appear to have been the most likely to champion the theory of evolution, particularly with his vast knowledge of paleontology and embryology. Instead, he chose to do battle with the evolutionists and to maintain stoutly his belief in the unchanging forms of created species. In his *Methods of Study in Natural History* (1863), Agassiz wrote: "I have devoted my whole life to the study of Nature, and yet a single sentence may express all that I have done. I have shown that there is a correspondence between the succession of Fishes in geological times and the different stages of their growth in the egg,—this is all."

Agassiz had done much more than he modestly claimed. In the age of Chautauqua speakers, he was a spellbinder. Above all, he was a teacher who was not only a dedicated scholar but also a friend to his students. With all of his talents as lecturer and author, he might have been a wealthy man, but he remained in debt all of his life and even mortgaged his house to support the museum at Harvard.

Agassiz wished above all to be remembered as a teacher. When he died in 1873, an unshaped boulder brought from the glacier of the Aar marked his grave at Boston's Mount Auburn Cemetery. On it were carved the words he had requested: "Agassiz the Teacher."

Bibliography

Agassiz, Louis. *Studies on Glaciers: Preceded by the Discourses of Neuchatel*. Translated and edited by Albert V. Carozzi. New York: Hafner Press, 1967. Carozzi's introduction is excellent. Included is a reprint of the atlas which Agassiz used.

Baird, Spencer Fullerton. *Correspondence Between Spencer Fullerton Baird and Louis Agassiz—Two Pioneer American Naturalists*. Edited by Elmer Charles Herber. Washington, D.C.: Smithsonian, 1964. Baird was the editor of the papers of the Smithsonian Institution and carried on extensive correspondence with Agassiz. The letters contained the latest news on discoveries in natural history.

Cooper, Lane. *Louis Agassiz as a Teacher*. Ithaca, N.Y.: Comstock, 1917. An excellent account of Agassiz's expertise as a teacher. Included are many anecdotes of classroom experiences, told by students.

Davenport, Guy, ed. *The Intelligence of Agassiz: A Specimen Book of Scientific Writings*. Boston: Beacon Press, 1963. The foreword by Alfred Romer is an excellent overview of the work of Agassiz. Davenport has selected Agassiz's most incisive works and introduces each with a skill which makes this slim volume invaluable.

Lurie, Edward. *Louis Agassiz: A Life in Science*. Chicago: University of Chicago Press, 1960. A persuasive interpretation of Agassiz and an exhaustive study of his papers. Lurie acknowledges Agassiz's weaknesses and pictures a genius with faults.

Marcou, Jules. *Life, Letters, and Works of Louis Agassiz*. 2 vols. New York: Macmillan, 1896. Valuable for range and accuracy of details, including an annotated list of American and European publications concerning Agassiz. Also included is a complete catalog of his 425 scientific papers.

Tharp, Louise Hall. *Adventurous Alliance: The Story of the Agassiz Family of Boston*. Boston: Little, Brown and Co., 1960. An account of the personal lives of Agassiz and his second wife, Elizabeth. An interesting story which relates something of the background of late nineteenth century Boston society. Also a treatise on education.

Raymond Lee Muncy

GEORGIUS AGRICOLA
Georg Bauer

Born: March 24, 1494; Glauchau, Saxony
Died: November 21, 1555; Chemnitz, Saxony
Area of Achievement: Geology
Contribution: Agricola was the forerunner of the new period of scientific investigation involving study and description of natural phenomena (especially geological in nature), preparation of metals from ores, and the development of mechanical procedures. He is regarded as the father of modern mineralogy.

Early Life

Born the son of a draper and named Georg Bauer, the young man Latinized his name, in the fashion of the time, to Georgius Agricola. Little of his life before 1514 is known, at which point he entered the University of Leipzig. In 1518, he was graduated, then went to Italy to continue his studies at the Universities of Bologna and Padua. His subsequent career began as a philologist, an expert in classical languages and the works of the classical writers. He then turned to medicine, took his degree at the University of Ferrare, and adopted medicine as a profession. While in Venice, he was employed for two years in the printing and publishing house of Aldus Manutius. At the Aldine Press, Agricola collaborated with John Clement, secretary to Thomas More. During this period, he also met and became friends with Desiderius Erasmus, who encouraged him to write and later published a number of his books. Coming home, Agricola began his medical practice in 1527 in Joachimsthal, in Bohemia, as city physician until 1533. In 1534, he moved to Chemnitz, another mining town, where he stayed for the rest of his life. In 1545, he was appointed Burgermeister.

Life's Work

As with his contemporary Paracelsus, Agricola's interest in mineralogy grew out of its possible connections with medicine and the diseases of the miners he treated. For more than two centuries, this combination of physician-mineralogist was to be prominent in the development of chemistry and geology. Agricola spent much time with the miners, in the mines and smelters, thus gaining an intimate knowledge of mining, mineralogy, and allied sciences. Most of his writings dealt with the geological sciences, although he wrote on many aspects of human endeavor. The beauty of his works lies in his use of illustrations, the woodcuts clear enough to let a modern builder re-create models of the ancient machines. His works were extremely difficult to decipher, particularly as they are written in Latin, a language ill equipped with appropriate terms for the mining trades. Since his

Library of Congress

ideas were based on German sources, he had to invent an entire new Latin vocabulary. As a result, some parts of the texts were difficult to understand even by contemporary readers. Only centuries after his death did Agricola get the credit he so richly deserved.

At Chemnitz, Agricola first became court historian, then city physician. Beginning in 1546, he published six works on mining and geology, a small work on the plague, and works on medical, religious, political, and historical subjects. It was a measure of his liberalism that, as a staunch Catholic, he served two Protestant dukes and worked diligently with other men of the Reformation. He served his dukes on many diplomatic and military missions, and he dedicated his major work, *De re metallica libri XII* (1556; English translation, 1912), to them.

Abandoning inductive speculation as he had learned it through his classical studies, Agricola disregarded biblical beliefs about the nature of the world, expressed his impatience with the alchemists, and concentrated on exploring the structure of the world on the basis of scientific observation. Such observation led him to the first adequate description of the part played by erosion in the shaping of mountain ranges, the origin of ores, the filling of rock interstices by circulating solutions, and the classifying of minerals on the basis of special physical characteristics, such as solubility and hardness.

Working with the miners in the two cities in which he had settled, Agricola began accumulating a massive amount of information on mining, smelting, the characteristics of ore deposits, and chemical analysis. *Bermannus sive de re metallica dialogus* (1530) was his first contribution to geology. It covered the rise of the mining industry in Germany and the early development of the great mining centers in the region of the Erzgebirge. Agricola discussed topics in mineralogy and mining, and various ores, such as silver, copper, and other metals. He showed some of the prejudices of his time, however, by dealing with the demons that supposedly haunted many of the mines. This was really an introduction to his greater work.

In 1546, he published *De ortu et causis subterraneorum*, treating the origin of ore deposits. After critically reviewing the opinions of early writers, particularly Aristotle, he rejected them, specifically the notion that metals are formed from watery vapors, and the alchemic view that all metals are composed of mercury and sulfur. He also criticized the astrological belief that the stars influence the earth's interior. Two major ideas came from this work: the origins of mountains and the origins of ore deposits. For mountains, Agricola found five means of formation: the eroding action of water, the heaping of sands by winds, subterranean winds, the actions of earthquakes, and volcanic fires. For ores, he presented the theory of lapidifying juices, solutions carrying dissolved minerals that, when cooled, left the deposits in the cracks of the rocks, thus giving rise to mineral veins. Here he predates two of the modern theories of ore deposits, the theory of ascension and the theory of lateral secretion.

Agricola's next important work, published in 1546, was *De natura fossilium* (English translation, 1955), in which he introduced a new basis for the classification of minerals (called "fossils" at that time). Agricola reviewed and rejected the systems of Aristotle, Avicenna, and others. His system was based on physical properties such as color, weight, transparency, taste, odor, texture, solubility, and combustibility. He carefully defined and explained the terms he developed. He also discussed the medicinal properties of the minerals.

Agricola's problem was understanding what he called "mista," composed of two or more fossils so intermingled as to be inseparable except by fire. His problem was a result of the alchemy of the time, the lack of a microscope, and the lack of real chemical analysis. Even without that knowledge, however, Agricola managed to remove the tales of supernatural forces in minerals and the theories of thunderstones and rocks with crystal power.

Agricola wrote three other works before his great opus: *De natura eorum quae effluent ex Terra* (1546), on subsurface waters and gases; *De veteribus et novis metallis* (1546), dealing with creatures that lived underground; and *De animantibus subterraneis* (1549), sketching the history and geographical distribution of the various metals as far as they had been known to the ancients.

De re metallica, his greatest work, concentrated on mining and metallurgy and contained an abundance of information on the conditions of the time, such as mine management, machinery used, and processes employed. The book is still in print, having the unique distinction of being translated and edited (1912) by President Herbert Hoover and his wife, Lou Henry Hoover. Indeed, it was the leading textbook for miners and metallurgists for two centuries. At a time when it was customary to hold industrial processes secret, Agricola published every practice and improvement he could find.

In *De re metallica*, Agricola's interests are all-consuming. Tracing the history of mineralogy and mining, Agricola addressed the earliest Greek and Roman sources, using them as a springboard for a major study in the locating of mines and a classification of the types of liquids emanating from them. In part of his opus, Agricola covered the specific working of metallic veins and ores in mines. Original contributions by him include the idea that rocks containing ores are older than the ores themselves and that the ores are deposited from solutions passing through fissures in the rocks—revolutionary ideas. He also suggested the procedure of using a magnetic compass for exploring and charting underground tunnels and provided the first real assessment of the wealth available for the three richest mines of the area. The work also includes hundreds of informative drawings showing the mechanical aspects of mining.

Agricola benefited greatly from the period of tolerance during which he worked. The religious wars of the period eroded this tolerance. Well regarded by his contemporaries, Agricola died in Chemnitz on November 21, 1555.

Summary

Georgius Agricola has been considered one of the most outstanding figures in the history of geological sciences. Johann Wolfgang von Goethe compared him to Roger Bacon. Alfred Werner called him the "father of mineralogy," and Karl von Vogelsang addressed him as the "forefather of geology." His works became the most comprehensive source on mining and metallurgy, acknowledged as the true beginning of geological sciences. Equally important, however, was that, in publishing that which tradition had retained as family and guild secrets, such as the process of smelting, he brought alert and innovative minds into the field of geology. Among those contemporaries were Conrad Gesner, who classified minerals on the basis of the form of the stone, gem, or fossil, avoiding all references to magic and miraculous properties of minerals, and Lazarus Ercker, who amplified Agricola's descriptions for separating precious metals through smelting. The instructions and descriptions that Agricola, Gesner, and Ercker prepared were so accurate that they would be used as handbooks for the next two centuries.

Agricola's works also helped establish, at Freiberg, a central source of mining and metallurgy knowledge, leading to a formalized, definite curriculum emphasizing observation and information-sharing. Agricola's work and his determination to use observation as the basis of science led to the use of scientific theories based on observation and experimentation.

Bibliography

Adams, Frank Dawson. *The Birth and Development of the Geological Sciences*. Reprint. New York: Dover, 1954. Traces the history of ideas and people contributing to the science of geology. Topics covered include the origins of metals, mountains, rivers, and oceans, and the nature of earthquakes.

Dibner, Bern. *Agricola on Metals*. Norwalk, Conn.: Burndy Library, 1958. Concise treatment of Agricola's life, with special emphasis on his major work *De re metallica*. Contains a book-by-book explanation of topics of interest. Excellent reproductions of original woodcuts.

Faul, Henry. *It Began with a Stone*. New York: John Wiley & Sons, 1983. A comprehensive work on the history of geology. Emphasizes people and their ideas, particularly as to how they arrived at their discoveries. Providing some of the original writings, the author shows how people such as Agricola thought.

Fenton, Carroll Lane, and Mildred Adams Fenton. *Giants of Geology*. New York: Doubleday, 1952. Details the thinking of the pioneers of geology, concentrating on the men who nurtured geological knowledge in exploring new areas of the world. Shows how ideas have altered over time, based on explorations and exquisite observations used to overthrow prejudices. Excellent references.

Geikie, Archibald. *The Founders of Geology.* New York: Doubleday, 1905. Tracing the slow growth of geology from ancient to modern cultures, the book deals with the controversies surrounding such geological ideas as volcanism, fossils, earth's origin, and geological succession.

Kranzberg, Melvin, and Carroll W. Pursell, Jr., eds. *Technology in Western Civilization.* Vol. 1, *The Emergence of Modern Industrial Society.* New York: Oxford University Press, 1967. This work portrays technology as one of the major determinants in the overall development of Western civilization. Attempting to integrate technological development with other aspects of society affected by it, the book deals nicely with the people and machines giving rise to modern society.

Singer, Charles, E. J. Holmyard, A. R. Hell, and Trevor Williams, eds. *A History of Technology.* Vol. 3, *From the Renaissance to the Industrial Revolution, c.1500-c.1750.* New York: Oxford University Press, 1957. A superb overview of the development and emergence of modern science during the Renaissance and later periods. Chronicles the development of technology and the people involved.

Arthur L. Alt

SAINT ALBERTUS MAGNUS

Born: c. 1200; Lauingen, Swabia
Died: November 15, 1280; Cologne
Areas of Achievement: Education and science
Contribution: Albertus expanded scientific knowledge through experimentation and observation. As an Aristotelian, he reconciled reason with revelation.

Early Life

Albertus was born at Lauingen in Swabia, the eldest son of the Count of Bollstädt. The exact date of his birth is not known; it could have been as early as 1193 or as late as 1207. Albertus matured during the most dynamic decades in medieval history, decades marked by the rule of great medieval sovereigns such as Pope Innocent III, Philip II in France, and Ferdinand III in Castile. The Albigensian and the Fourth crusades were fought at this time, and in England, King John signed the Magna Carta. The dates, places, and content of Albertus' education are still open to speculation. Most scholars believe that he studied the liberal arts for some months in 1222 at the newly founded University of Padua.

As the University of Padua had just broken away from the University of Bologna over the issue of civil versus canon law, it would appear that Albertus' father planned for him to become a civil lawyer. That would account, too, for the strong objections of Albertus' family when, in 1223, at about the age of sixteen, he joined the Dominican Order.

As a novice, Albertus studied theology, probably at Bologna, where he was immersed in the writings of theologians ranging from Saint Augustine to Robert Grosseteste. Despite the constitutions of his order, issued in 1228, which forbade the study of books written by pagans and philosophers, Albertus knew a large number of these works, which profoundly influenced him. He read the works of Averroës, Avicenna, Pliny, Plato, and especially Aristotle. He also knew Pythagorean arithmetic, though Roger Bacon would later claim that Albertus was never a mathematician.

Life's Work

In 1228, Albertus left Bologna for Cologne, where he began his career as a teacher. In 1233, his order assigned him the lectorship in Hildesheim. Subsequently, he taught at Fribourg, Ratisbon, and Strasbourg. In 1240, he went to the University of Paris, where he earned his degree as a doctor of theology. While there, he ensured his reputation as one of the great minds of his age as a result of two diverse activities.

First, he began work on his commentaries on Aristotle, which ultimately included treatises on physics, metaphysics, logic, psychology, geography,

Library of Congress

zoology, botany, mineralogy, astrology, alchemy, chiromancy, and celestial phenomena. So well conceived and detailed were these writings that Albertus was quoted as an authority even during his lifetime. With this work, Albertus contributed significantly to the creation of Christian Aristotelianism.

Second, in 1240, as a result of polemical attacks upon the Talmud, Blanche of Castile and her son, Louis IX, called for a public debate of the merits of those attacks. Albertus was one of seven people chosen to discuss the issue. Because of this debate, Albertus' skills as a negotiator were in frequent demand.

Twice he settled disputes between the citizens of Cologne and Archbishop Conrad von Hochstein, typical examples of the struggle between feudal authority and the rising power of the middle-class townsmen. Albertus negotiated a trade agreement between Cologne and Utrecht. He settled a property dispute between Mecklenburg and the Knights of Saint John at the request of Pope Clement IV.

After receiving his doctor's degree, Albertus stayed in Paris, where he taught theology at the university from 1242 to 1248. This is the period when Thomas Aquinas and Siger de Brabant studied with him. In 1248, the Dominicans sent Albertus to Cologne to found and administer the first Dominican school in Germany. There he collaborated with Thomas and others in the formulation of a standard course of study for the schools of the order. Later, he was appointed for three years the provincial over all German Dominicans.

Albertus' administrative ability must have been equal to the quality of his teaching and negotiating, because the pope, over the objections of both Albertus and the general of the Dominicans, Humbert of Romans, appointed Albertus Bishop of Ratisbona in 1260, a position that he resigned in 1262. Almost immediately thereafter, Pope Urban IV sent him to preach the Eighth Crusade, an assignment which lasted two years. In 1264, he returned to teaching, first at Würzburg and then in Strasbourg, after which he finally returned to Cologne in 1272.

He left this oft-sought, much-desired seclusion only a few more times before his death in 1280; the first time was to attend the council at Lyons in 1274. The second occurred in 1277, when Albertus went to Paris to defend his former student Thomas (who had died in 1274) and Aristotelianism, under attack for heresy. As Albertus may have been past eighty at this time and was apparently not in good health, this action clearly indicates his dedication to Aristotelian thought and his support of Thomas.

In addition to boundless energy and practicality in everyday affairs, Albertus possessed an encyclopedic mind, unflagging curiosity, and an undaunted commitment to scholarly endeavors, as is illustrated by the subjects about which he wrote. A prolific writer, he produced at least thirty-eight volumes on interests ranging from alchemy to zoology. Albertus' scientific approach was rooted in experimentation and observation rather than in philosophical speculation and revelation. He had no patience with those who accepted dogmatic knowledge without investigation. Where experience disagreed with accepted dogma, he followed experience, preferably his own. While conceding that all things must ultimately be attributed to divine will, he argued that God worked through nature, which could be understood through reason.

More specifically, Albertus thought that there were two kinds of knowledge, that of theology, faith, and revelation and that of philosophy and natural reason. According to Albertus, there was no contradiction. Instead, he saw each activity as separate but not exclusive of the other; he harmonized the whole, using each kind of knowledge in its appropriate sphere of human inquiry. Albertus began all of his investigations with Aristotle's work and mindful of the Christian faith. Anchored in these, he allowed his empirical observations to refine, redefine, elaborate, and correct. He felt free to exercise reason on all natural phenomena.

De vegetabilibus et plantis, written around 1250, became the chief source of biological knowledge in Europe for the next three hundred years. Albertus relied almost exclusively on observation. He noted how ecological conditions, such as heat, light, and moisture, affected the way things grew. His study of plants led him close to an understanding of mutation and species modification, something he could not transfer to his investigation of animals, probably because it brought him too close to man.

De animalibus (thirteenth century) recorded Albertus' thinking on zoology. In it, his observations about German whaling and fishing were outstanding. To the standard Aristotelian catalog he added descriptions of animals that he had observed in northern Europe. Unfortunately, his understanding of animals, especially the reproductive process, fell prey to the standard misconceptions of his day; for example, he thought that the birth of monstrosities resulted from "defective female matter" which the male "vital heat" could not overcome. Nevertheless, he identified correctly the function of the umbilical cord and the placenta. Through observation, he disproved many of the traditional mystical origins and theological definitions of animals.

It was in his works *De mineralibus et rebus metallicis* (c. 1260; *Book of Minerals*, 1967) and *De causis proporietatum elementorum* (thirteenth century), however, that Albertus made his most original contributions. In them, he scientifically described various precious stones and minerals, although he often included descriptions of mystical properties. He also correctly explained why sea fossils could be found high on a mountainside. Finally, Albertus believed that the world was a sphere and held the near-heretical notion that people lived on the "underside" of that sphere; yet he still believed that Earth was the center of the universe, with all else revolving around it.

Albertus remains one of the greatest medieval theorists on physical science. Although many of his inquiries produced traditional answers, his methodology was a harbinger of modern science. He provided the framework for an understanding of the operations of the physical world, which he saw as a system of activity and constant change; this conception was contrary to the thinking of many of his contemporaries, who defined the world in static terms. He died in Cologne in 1280.

Summary

The life of Albertus Magnus, the "Christian Aristotle," spanned most of the thirteenth century. He was part of the great outburst of philosophical speculation which characterized the medieval mind. He dealt effectively with at least twelve different popes, beginning with Innocent III, popes who often challenged his methodology and thought. Albertus became the most learned man and the greatest teacher of his day; he is still the patron saint of Catholic schools.

Because of the overwhelming quantity and quality of his work and because of his excellence as a teacher, Albertus earned the titles "Magnus" and "Universal Teacher." A man of common sense, with an insatiable and healthy curiosity, he sought truth, accepted it when he found it, and conveyed it honestly to his students. Roger Bacon, who was by no means one of Albertus' supporters, conceded that Albertus was one of the greatest scholars of their day. Nevertheless, many were the pedestrian minds who accused Albertus of magic and consorting with the Devil, thinking that such breadth of knowledge could not have been gained in any other way. At times, he was considered a pantheist, although this doctrine would never have appealed to Albertus, who was a man deeply committed to God as the creator and source of all knowledge. In his belief, to understand nature was to understand God.

Although his teaching and administrative career was primarily confined to Germany, Albertus' reputation was European. While he reflected much of the temper of his age, he also helped to create it. More than anyone else, he constructed the Scholastic world system. He awakened the scientific spirit that would dominate the intellectual life of subsequent centuries. Little wonder that his contemporaries called him "Magnus."

Bibliography

Brandt, William J. *The Shape of Medieval History: Studies in Modes of Perception*. New Haven, Conn.: Yale University Press, 1966. This is an excellent study of medieval perceptions of nature, human nature, and human action, which illustrates how those perceptions defined the world for the medieval thinker. Contains extensive explanatory notes, which offset the lack of a bibliography.

Crombie, A. C. *Medieval and Early Modern Science*. Vol. 1. Garden City, N.Y.: Doubleday and Co., 1959. This is an excellent analysis of Albertus' contributions to the sciences and empirical methodology. Highly readable and contains an excellent bibliography.

Durant, Will. *The Story of Civilization*. Vol. 4, *The Age of Faith: A History of Medieval Civilization—Christian, Islamic, and Judaic—from Constantine to Dante, A.D. 325-1300*. New York: Simon and Schuster, 1950. An enjoyable work of popular history, it provides an excellent introduction to Albertus. Contains a standard bibliography and a detailed table of contents.

Gilson, Étienne. *History of Christian Philosophy in the Middle Ages*. London: Sheed and Ward, 1955. Gilson is the leading modern follower of Saint Thomas Aquinas, who thought that truth was perennial and, like Albertus, that there need not be a contradiction between reason and faith.

Haskins, Charles Homer. *The Rise of Universities*. Ithaca, N.Y.: Cornell University Press, 1923. Haskins interpretively outlines the rise of the medieval university, commenting briefly on Albertus' role. This study sparked a generation's study of medieval education.

Heer, Friedrich. *The Intellectual History of Europe*. Translated by Jonathan Steinberg. Cleveland, Ohio: World Publishing Co., 1968. An excellent analysis of the development of Western thought, with Albertus seen as a pivotal figure. This is a detailed scholarly study; the sources must be culled from copious notes.

Leff, Gordon. *Medieval Thought: St. Augustine to Ockham*. Baltimore: Penguin Books, 1958. Leff gives the reader an easily understood description of the development of the medieval mind. Describes Albertus' contributions as a synthesizer, an experimenter, an Aristotelian who reconciled reason and faith; according to Leff, he foreshadowed René Descartes and John Locke in methodology. Limited bibliography.

Thorndike, Lynn. *A History of Magic and Experimental Science*. Vols. 1 and 2, *The First Thirteen Centuries of Our Era*. New York: Columbia University Press, 1923. Thorndike remains one of the great historians of science. In this work, he describes Albertus' empirical method.

Weisheipl, James A. *The Development of Physical Theory in the Middle Ages*. Ann Arbor: University of Michigan Press, 1971. Weisheipl stresses Albertus' elaboration and extension of Aristotelian science, particularly in physics. The reader is persuaded that there was much originality in medieval scientific thought. The bibliography for this short, perceptive, and interpretive essay contains the standard works on the history of science.

Shirley F. Fredricks

ALCMAEON

Born: c. 510 B.C.; Croton, Magna Graecia (southern Italy)
Died: c. 430 B.C.; place unknown
Areas of Achievement: Medicine and philosophy
Contribution: Alcmaeon was one of the earliest Greeks known to have written on medicine and the first to have practiced scientific dissection. He held that the brain is the central organ of sensation and that health is the result of an equilibrium of qualities or forces in the body.

Early Life

Of Alcmaeon's early life almost nothing is known, except that his father's name was Peirithous and that he was a native of Croton (Greek Crotona), a coastal town inside the "toe" of Italy. Even Alcmaeon's dates are uncertain. According to Aristotle, he lived during the old age of the philosopher Pythagoras, whose life spanned much of the sixth century B.C. and who died about 490 or later. It was once assumed that, as a younger contemporary of Pythagoras, Alcmaeon probably should be placed in the sixth century. It is now widely held, however, largely from the evidence of his ideas, that he probably lived in the fifth century. The evidence at the disposal of modern scholars is not sufficient to fix the date of his lifetime more precisely.

Croton was a Greek city founded by Achaeans from mainland Greece in 710 B.C. It had a fine harbor and enjoyed extensive commerce. As a result, it became the wealthiest and most powerful city in Magna Graecia (the Greek name for southern Italy), especially after its forces defeated and completely destroyed its enemy, the neighboring city of Sybaris, in 510. It boasted the most splended temple in southern Italy, the temple of Hera Lacinia, which drew large numbers of Greeks to a great annual religious assembly. Croton was renowned for its devotion to gymnastics; one of its citizens, Milon, became the most famous athlete in Greece, having won the victory in wrestling at Olympia six times. Croton is said to have produced more Olympic victors than any other city.

Croton was also the home of a well-known school of medicine, which was perhaps the earliest in Greece and which long retained its reputation. The city enjoyed the distinction of producing the finest physicians in Greece, of whom the most prominent was Democedes, regarded as the best physician of his day (the latter half of the sixth century B.C.). His fame carried him to Aegina, Athens, and Samos, where he was employed by the tyrant Polycrates, and to Persia (as a prisoner), where he cured both King Darius the Great and his wife, Atossa, before he escaped, returning to Croton to marry the daughter of Milon.

Croton was also known as the home of the philosopher Pythagoras and his followers. Born in Samos, Pythagoras emigrated to Croton about 530, where

Library of Congress

he formed a religious brotherhood composed of about three hundred young men. Pythagoras quickly gained influence over the political affairs of the city, but growing opposition to his order led to his retirement from Croton. In the latter half of the fifth century, a democratic revolution resulted in a massacre of nearly all the members of the order. Alcmaeon is said by some ancient authors to have been a disciple of Pythagoras, but it is likely that this belief was based only on inferences from the similarities of some of his doctrines to those of the Pythagoreans. Aristotle compares his theory of opposites with that of the Pythagoreans but says that Alcmaeon either borrowed this idea from them or they took it from him. There is, in fact, no definitive evidence that associates Alcmaeon with the Pythagoreans. He lived during the period in which the Pythagorean brotherhood flourished at Croton, and he probably knew of the Pythagoreans and their beliefs. His precise relationship to them, however, is not known. Diogenes Laertius reports that Alcmaeon wrote mostly on medicine, and it has been inferred from this statement that he was a physician. Given Croton's reputation as a medical center, it is not unlikely. He wrote on physics and astronomy as well, however, and in this respect he resembles the Ionian philosophers, some of whom were interested in medicine. He was certainly a natural philosopher, interested in science and medicine; he may or may not have been a physician.

Life's Work

Alcmaeon lived in the pre-Socratic period, when the study of physiology was merely a part of philosophy. Only later did Hippocrates separate medicine from philosophy. Greek medical theory, in fact, grew out of philosophical speculation rather than the practice of medicine. Alcmaeon's contributions include both cosmological conjecture and anatomical research. He was credited in antiquity with having written the first treatise on natural philosophy. The book is no longer extant, but some idea of its contents can be gleaned from portions that were summarized by later writers. In the opening sentence of the work, Alcmaeon declared that the gods alone have certain knowledge, while for men only inference from things seen is possible. Thus, he eschewed all-encompassing, oversimplified hypotheses in favor of careful observation as the basis of understanding nature.

Nevertheless, Alcmaeon shared with the Ionian philosophers an interest in natural speculation. Thus, he posited a microcosmic-macrocosmic relationship between man and the universe. He believed that the human soul was immortal because it was continuously in motion like the heavenly bodies, which he thought divine and immortal because they moved continuously and eternally in circles. While the heavenly bodies are immortal, however, men perish because "they cannot join the beginning to the end." Alcmaeon seems to mean by this that human life is not circular but linear and thus is not eternally renewed but runs down and dies when its motion ceases.

Alcmaeon developed a theory of opposites, according to which human beings have within them pairs of opposing forces, such as black and white, bitter and sweet, good and bad, large and small. He may well have been indebted to the Pythagoreans, who posited pairs of contrary qualities on mathematical lines (or they may have borrowed the notion from him). Alcmaeon, however, applied his theory particularly to health and disease. He defined health as a balance or equilibrium (*isonomia*) of opposing forces in the body (for example, warm and cold, bitter and sweet, wet and dry). He explained disease as the excess or predominance (*monarchia*) of one of these qualities or pairs of opposites that upsets the balance. This predominance could be caused by an excess or deficiency of food or by such external factors as climate, locality, fatigue, or exertion. Alcmaeon probably based this theory on his observation of factional struggles in Greek city-states, and he may have been influenced by the growth of democratic political ideas. Of all Alcmaeon's theories, this concept of opposites was to be the most influential in later Greek thought. The Hippocratic treatise *Peri archaies ietrikes* (c. 430-400 B.C.; *Ancient Medicine*) defends and elaborates this explanation.

Alcmaeon's theoretical speculation was balanced by a notable empirical tendency. It is this mixture of theory and observation that gives his work a distinctive and even pioneering nature. Alcmaeon, like many pre-Socratic philosophers, was interested in physiology, but he appears to have been the first to test his theories by examination of the body. In a celebrated case, he cut out the eye of an animal (whether dead or alive is uncertain). He was apparently interested in observing the substances of which the eye was composed. Whether he dissected the eye itself is not known. He also discovered (or inferred the existence of) the channels that connect the eye to the brain (probably the optic nerves).

There is no evidence that Alcmaeon ever dissected human corpses, and it is unlikely that he did so. He believed that the eye contained fire (which could be seen when the eye was hit) and water (which dissection revealed to have come from the brain). He concluded that there were similar passages connecting the other sense organs to the brain, and he described the passages connecting the brain to the mouth, nose, and ears (and quite possibly was the first to discover the Eustachian tubes). He thought that these channels were hollow and carried *pneuma* (air). Alcmaeon concluded that the brain provided the sensations of sight, hearing, smell, and taste, for he noticed that when a concussion occurred, the senses were affected. Similarly, when the passages were blocked, communication between the brain and the sense organs was cut off. Plato followed Alcmaeon in holding that the brain is the central organ of thought and feeling, but Aristotle and many other philosophers continued to attribute that function to the heart. Alcmaeon also differed from most contemporary philosophers in distinguishing between sensation and thought. He observed that sensation is common to all animals, while only man possesses intelligence.

According to Alcmaeon, whether the body was awake or asleep had to do with the amount of blood in the veins. Sleep was caused by the blood retiring to the larger blood vessels, while waking was the result of the blood being rediffused throughout the body. Alcmaeon was also interested in embryology, and he opened birds' eggs and examined the development of the embryo. He believed that the head, not the heart, was the first to develop. He resorted to speculation rather than observation in holding that human semen has its origin in the brain. He explained the sterility of mules by the theory that the seed produced by the male was too fine and cold, while the womb of the female did not open, and hence conception was prevented.

Summary

Alcmaeon is recognized as an important figure in the development of the biological sciences in ancient Greece. Although his date is uncertain and few details regarding either his career or his scientific methods are known, it is clear that he exercised considerable influence on subsequent Greek writers in the fields of medicine and biology. He introduced ideas that were later elaborated by Empedocles, Democritus, several Hippocratic writers, Plato, and Aristotle, among others. His idea that health is a balance of opposing forces in the body, although later modified, was accepted for many hundreds of years. Alcmaeon has often been called the father of embryology, anatomy, physiology, and experimental psychology. While such titles may be unwarranted, in each of these areas Alcmaeon did make significant contributions.

Regardless of whether Alcmaeon was a physician, he was one of the earliest Greeks to formulate medical theories. Many of his ideas were speculative and borrowed from earlier philosophers. Although influenced by the Pythagoreans, he avoided their mysticism, and he recognized the limitations of scientific inference. His medical theory did not grow out of medical practice but always retained a close affinity with philosophy; such theories tended to have little influence on the general practice of Greek medicine. Still, Alcmaeon's anatomical investigation (particularly his dissection of the eye) and his recognition that the senses are connected with the brain established him as a genuine pioneer in the development of Greek medical science.

Bibliography

Codellas, P. S. "Alcmaeon of Croton: His Life, Work, and Fragments." *Proceedings of the Royal Society of Medicine* 25 (1931/1932): 1041-1046. A brief but comprehensive discussion of Alcmaeon's life and contributions, published by the Royal Society of Medicine's Section on the History of Medicine.

Guthrie, W. K. C. *A History of Greek Philosophy*. Vol. 1. Cambridge: Cambridge University Press, 1962. A discussion of the evidence for Alcmaeon's dates and an examination of his medical, physiological, and cosmological theories (particularly his doctrine of the soul) by a leading expert on Greek philosophy.

Jones, W. H. S. *Philosophy and Medicine in Ancient Greece*. New York: Arno Press, 1946, reprint 1979. Provides translations of the most important sources for Alcmaeon's life and doctrines, and discusses Alcmaeon's relationship to Plato and Aristotle.

Lloyd, Geoffrey. "Alcmaeon and the Early History of Dissection." *Sudhoffs Archiv* 59 (1975): 113-147. A detailed examination of the evidence for Alcmaeon's use of dissection, which Lloyd believes Alcmaeon to have practiced in a very limited manner rather than systematically. Explores as well the history of early Greek dissection after Alcmaeon.

Sigerist, Henry E., ed. *A History of Medicine*. Vol. 2, *Early Greek, Hindu, and Persian Medicine*. New York: Oxford University Press, 1961. A general discussion of Alcmaeon and his work in the context of early Greek medicine and philosophy. Valuable for its general treatment of Greek medicine and its background.

Gary B. Ferngren

JEAN LE ROND D'ALEMBERT

Born: November 17, 1717; Paris, France
Died: October 29, 1783; Paris, France
Areas of Achievement: Mathematics, physics, philosophy, and music
Contribution: A pioneer in the use of differential calculus, d'Alembert applied his mathematical genius to solve problems in mechanics. He provided valuable assistance with the *Encyclopédie* and wrote a number of treatises on musical theory.

Early Life

On the night of November 17, 1717, Mme Claudine-Alexandrine Guérin, Marquise de Tencin, gave birth to a son whom she promptly abandoned on the steps of the Church of Saint-Jean-Le-Rond. There, he was baptized with the name of the church; he was then sent to the Maison de la Coucher, from which he went to a foster home in Picardy. When his father, Louis-Camus Destouches, a military officer, returned to Paris, he sought his son and arranged for the child to be cared for by Mme Rousseau, the wife of a glazier. D'Alembert would always regard Mme Rousseau as his real mother and would continue to live with her until 1765, when illness compelled him to seek new quarters in the home of Julie de Lespinasse.

Destouches continued to watch over his illegitimate child, sending him to private schools; when Destouches died in 1726, he left the boy a legacy of twelve hundred livres a year. The sum, though not luxurious, guaranteed him an independence he cherished throughout his life. Through the interest of the Destouches family, the young man entered the Jansenist Collège des Quatre-Nations, where he took the name Jean-Baptiste Daremberg, later changing it, perhaps for euphony, to d'Alembert. Although he, like many other Enlightenment figures, abandoned the religious training he received there, he never shed the Cartesian influence that dominated the school.

After receiving his *baccalauréat* in 1735, he spent two years studying law, receiving a license to practice in 1738. Neither jurisprudence nor medicine, to which he devoted a year, held his interest. He turned to mathematics, for which he had a natural talent. At the age of twenty-two, he submitted his first paper to the Académie des Sciences; in that piece, he corrected a number of errors in Father Charles Reyneau's *Analyse demontrée* (1714). A second paper, on refraction and fluid mechanics, followed the next year, and in May, 1741, he was made an adjunct member of the Académie des Sciences.

Life's Work

Two years later, d'Alembert published a major contribution to mechanics, *Traité de dynamique* (1743), which includes his famous principle stating that the force which acts on a body in a system is the sum of the forces within the

Library of Congress

system restraining it and the external forces acting on that system. Although Isaac Newton and Johann Bernoulli had already offered similar observations, neither had expressed the matter so simply. The effect of d'Alembert's principle was to convert a problem of dynamics to one of statics, making it easier to solve. The treatise is characteristic of d'Alembert's work in several ways: It illustrates his exceptional facility with mathematics; it reveals a desire to find universal laws in a discipline; and it indicates his ability to reduce complex matters to simple components. Over the next several years, he wrote a number of other innovative works in both mathematics and fluid mechanics.

At the same time that d'Alembert was establishing himself as one of Europe's leading mathematicians—in 1752 Frederick the Great offered him the presidency of the Berlin Academy—he emerged as a leading figure of the Parisian salons. In 1743, he was introduced to the influential Mme du Deffand, who would secure his election to the Académie Française in 1754. He remained a fixture of her assemblies until Julie de Lespinasse, whom he met there, established her own salon following a quarrel with the older woman. Later in the 1740's, he also joined the gatherings at the homes of Mme Marie-Thérèse Rodet Geoffrin and Anne-Louise Bénédicte de Bourbon, Duchesse du Maine. Not striking in appearance—he was short and, according to a contemporary, "of rather undistinguished features, with a fresh complexion that tends to ruddiness," his eyes small and his mouth large—he compensated for his looks with his excellent ability with mimicry and his lively conversation.

While enjoying the female-dominated world of the salons, d'Alembert was also meeting a number of important male intellectuals, with whom he dined weekly at the Hôtel du Panier Fleuri—Denis Diderot, Jean-Jacques Rousseau (no relation to his stepmother), and Étienne Bonnot de Condillac. He probably also knew Gua de Malves, a fellow mathematician and member of the Académie des Sciences, who was chosen as the first editor of the *Encyclopédie* (1751-1772), and Malves may have been the one who introduced d'Alembert to the project; after Malves resigned, d'Alembert was named coeditor with Diderot.

D'Alembert did not plan to assume as much responsibility for the work as his coeditor. He wrote to Samuel Formey in September, 1749:

> I never intended to have a hand in [the *Encyclopédie*] except for what has to do with mathematics and physical astronomy. I am in a position to do only that, and besides, I do not intend to condemn myself for ten years to the tedium of seven or eight folios.

It was Diderot who conceived of the work as a summation of human knowledge, but d'Alembert's involvement extended well beyond the mathematical articles that the title page credits to him.

His contributions took many forms. He used his scientific contacts to solicit articles, and his connection with the world of the salons, which Diderot did not frequent, permitted him to enlist support among the aristocracy and upper middle class. Not only was such backing politically important, given the controversial nature of the enterprise, but also the financial assistance d'Alembert secured may well have prevented its collapse. Mme Geoffrin alone is reported to have donated more than 100,000 livres.

Also significant are the fifteen hundred articles that d'Alembert wrote, including the important *Discours préliminaire* (1751; *Preliminary Discourse to the Encyclopedia of Diderot*, 1963). Praised by all the great French intellectuals as well as Frederick the Great, it seeks to explain the purpose and plan of the *Encyclopédie* by showing the links between disciplines and tracing the progress of knowledge from the Renaissance to 1750. In its view of the Enlightenment as the culmination of progress in thought, it reflects the philosophes' optimistic, humanistic attitude. D'Alembert's own understanding of the role of the philosopher and the nature of learning also emerges clearly in this essay. For him, "The universe is but a vast ocean, on the surface of which we perceive certain islands more or less large, whose link with the continent is hidden from us." The goal of the scientist is to discover, not invent, these concealed links, and mathematics would provide the means for establishing these connections. Just as physicists of the twentieth century seek the one force that impels all nature, so d'Alembert sought the single principle that underlies all knowledge.

In 1756, d'Alembert went to Geneva to visit Voltaire, his closest friend among the philosophes, and to gather information for an article on this center of Calvinism. Already in "Collège" d'Alembert had antagonized the Church by criticizing ecclesiastical control of education. "Genève," with its intended praise of Protestant ministers, provoked sharp protests from the Catholic establishment in France, and Calvinists were upset as well by d'Alembert's portrait of them as virtual agnostics. Opposition to the *Encyclopédie* was growing in court circles; in March, 1759, permission to publish would be withdrawn. Never as daring as Voltaire or Diderot, d'Alembert resigned as coeditor in 1758, despite protests from his friends and associates. He did, however, continue to write articles on mathematics and science.

While the controversy surrounding the enterprise, especially "Genève," was the primary reason for d'Alembert's distancing himself from the *Encyclopédie*, another important factor was his growing disagreement with Diderot over the direction the work was taking. By 1758, Diderot, who had himself published a treatise on mathematics—*Mémoires sur différens sujets de mathématiques* (1748)—had come to believe that no further progress was possible in that field, so he rejected his coeditor's emphasis on mathematics as the key to knowledge, stating that "the reign of mathematics is over." D'Alembert's Cartesian theories also troubled Diderot. Like René Descartes, d'Alembert believed that matter is inert; Diderot disagreed. While d'Alembert maintained that the most precise sciences were those like geometry that relied on abstract principles derived from reason, Diderot regarded experimentation and observation—empiricism—as the best guarantees of reliability. For d'Alembert, the more abstruse the science the better, for he sought to solve problems. Diderot preferred knowledge that directly affected life. In later years, Diderot continued to praise d'Alembert's mathematical abilities, and d'Alembert unsuccessfully tried to secure Diderot's election to the Académie Française, but the two remained only distant friends.

Withdrawing from the *Encyclopédie* did not signal d'Alembert's rejection of the Enlightenment. Instead, he sought to use the Académie Française as a forum to promulgate the views of the philosophes. His first speech before the Académie Française urged toleration and freedom of expression, and in 1769 he nearly succeeded in having the body offer a prize for the best poem on the subject of "The Progress of Reason Under Louis XIV," the notion of such progress being a fundamental tenet of the Enlightenment. In 1768, when the King of Denmark, Christian VII, visited the Académie Française, and again in March, 1771, when Gustavus III of Sweden attended a session, d'Alembert spoke of the benefits of enlightened policies. Through his influence in the salons, he arranged for the election of nine philosophes to the Académie Française between 1760 and 1770, and a number of others sympathetic to their cause also entered because of d'Alembert. Elected permanent secretary of the body in 1772, he thereafter used his official eulogies to attack the enemies of the Enlightenment and to encourage advanced ideas.

D'Alembert also continued to publish. The first three volumes of *Opuscules mathématiques* (1761-1780) contain much original work on hydrodynamics, lenses, and astronomy. His anonymous *Sur la destruction des Jésuites en France* (1765; *An Account of the Destruction of the Jesuits in France*, 1766), occasioned by the suppression of the order, discusses the danger of linking civil and ecclesiastical power because theological disputes then disturb domestic peace. In addition to attacking the Jesuits, d'Alembert urged the suppression of their rivals, the Jansenists.

Active as he was in the Académie Française, d'Alembert's last years were marked by physical and emotional pain. Devoted to Julie de Lespinasse, he was doubly distressed by her death in 1776 and the discovery of love letters to her from the Comte de Guibert and the Marquis de Mora. As permanent secretary of the Académie Française, he was entitled to a small apartment in the Louvre, and there he spent the final seven years of his life, which ended on October 29, 1783. Although he produced little original work of his own during this period, he remained an important correspondent of Voltaire and Frederick the Great, urging the monarch to grant asylum to those persecuted for their views. He also encouraged young mathematicians such as Joseph-Louis Lagrange, Pierre-Simon Laplace, and the Marquis de Condorcet.

Summary

Voltaire sometimes doubted Jean Le Rond d'Alembert's zeal for the cause of Enlightenment, and d'Alembert's distancing himself from the *encyclopédistes* reveals that he was not one to take great risks. He observed that "honest men can no longer fight except by hiding behind the hedges, but from that position they can fire some good shots at the wild beasts infesting the country." From his post in the salons and the Académie Française, he worked, as he told Voltaire, "to gain esteem for the little flock" of philosophes.

If Voltaire could accuse d'Alembert of excessive caution, d'Alembert could in turn charge Voltaire with toadying to the powerful. In his 1753 *Essai sur les gens de lettres*, d'Alembert urged writers to rely solely on their talents, and he reminded the nobility that intellectuals were their equals. "I am determined never to put myself in the service of anyone and to die as free as I have lived," he wrote Voltaire. Neither Frederick the Great's repeated invitations to assume the presidency of the Berlin Academy nor Catherine the Great's offer of 100,000 livres a year to tutor her son Grand Duke Paul could lure him away from France and independence.

In both his life and thought he was loyal to the ideals of the philosophes, so it is fitting that Ernst Cassirer should choose him as the representative of the Enlightenment and call him "one of the most important scholars of the age and one of its intellectual spokesmen." His belief in the ability of reason to solve any problem epitomizes the view of eighteenth century intellectuals, but he also recognized the role of experimentation and imagination. In his *Eléméns de musique théorique et practique suivant les principes de M. Rameau* (1752), d'Alembert dissented from Jean-Philippe Rameau's view that one can devise mathematical rules for composition. As in his article on elocution in the *Encyclopédie*, he argued that rules are necessary, but only genius can elevate a work beyond mediocrity. Excellent scientist though he was, he ranked the artist above the philosopher.

Bibliography

Cassirer, Ernst. *The Philosophy of the Enlightenment*. Princeton, N.J.: Princeton University Press, 1951. A translation of Cassirer's 1932 book in German, this work explores the way the Enlightenment looked at nature, psychology, religion, history, society, and aesthetics. Much, *inter alia*, about d'Alembert.

Essar, Dennis F. *The Language Theory, Epistemology, and Aesthetics of Jean Lerond d'Alembert*. Oxford, England: Voltaire Foundation at the Taylor Institution, 1976. A study of d'Alembert's philosophy. Argues that d'Alembert's "position in the Enlightenment remains of central, pivotal importance." Also treats d'Alembert's mathematical and scientific contributions.

Grimsley, Ronald. *Jean d'Alembert, 1717-83*. Oxford, England: Clarendon Press, 1963. A topical study of d'Alembert's contributions to the *Encyclopédie*, his relations with other philosophers, and his own views. Largely ignores the scientific and mathematical aspects of d'Alembert's career.

Hankins, Thomas L. *Jean d'Alembert: Science and the Enlightenment*. Oxford, England: Clarendon Press, 1970. An ideal complement to Grimsley's book, for it concentrates on the science and the mathematics. Relates d'Alembert's achievements to those of other scientists and the role of science to that of philosophy in the eighteenth century.

Pappas, John Nicholas. *Voltaire and d'Alembert*. Bloomington: Indiana University Press, 1962. Drawing heavily on the correspondence between the two, this study seeks to rectify the view, fostered in large part by Voltaire, that d'Alembert was a hesitant follower of the older intellectual. Notes that the influence was mutual and shows where the two differed.

Van Treese, Glen Joseph. *D'Alembert and Frederick the Great: A Study of Their Relationship*. New York: Learned Publications, 1974. Treats the origin, nature, and consequences of the friendship between d'Alembert and the Prussian ruler. Offers a portrait of the two men and of their age.

Joseph Rosenblum

ALHAZEN

Born: 965; Basra, Iraq
Died: 1039; Cairo, Egypt
Areas of Achievement: Physics, astronomy, mathematics, and medicine
Contribution: Alhazen, Islam's greatest scientist, devoted his life to physics, astronomy, mathematics, and medicine. His treatise *Optics*, in which he deftly used experiments and advanced mathematics to understand the action of light, exerted a profound influence on many European natural philosophers.

Early Life

Abu 'Ali al-Ḥasan ibn al-Haytham (commonly known as Alhazen, the Latinized form of his first name, al-Ḥasan) was born in Basra in 965. He was given a traditional Muslim education, but at an early age he became perplexed by the variety of religious beliefs and sects, because he was convinced of the unity of truth. When he was older, he concluded that truth could be attained only in doctrines whose matter was sensible and whose form was rational. He found such doctrines in the writings of Aristotle and in natural philosophy and mathematics.

By devoting himself completely to learning, Alhazen achieved fame as a scholar and was given a political post at Basra. In an attempt to obtain a better position, he claimed that he could construct a machine to regulate the flooding of the Nile. The Fatimid caliph al-Hakim, wishing to use this sage's expertise, persuaded him to move to Cairo. Alhazen, to fulfill his boast, was trapped into heading an engineering mission to Egypt's southern border. On his way to Aswan, he began to have doubts about his plan, for he observed excellently designed and perfectly constructed buildings along the Nile, and he realized that his scheme, if it were possible, would have already been carried out by the creators of these impressive structures. His misgivings were confirmed when he discovered that the cataracts south of Aswan made flood control impossible. Convinced of the impracticability of his plan, and fearing the wrath of the eccentric and volatile caliph, Alhazen pretended to be mentally deranged; upon his return to Cairo, he was confined to his house until al-Hakim's death in 1021.

Alhazen then took up residence in a small domed shrine near the Azhar Mosque. Having been given back his previously sequestered property, he resumed his activities as a writer and teacher. He may have earned his living by copying mathematical works, including Euclid's *Stoicheia* (c. fourth century B.C.; *Elements*) and Ptolemy's *Mathēmatikē suntaxis* (c. A.D. 150; *Almagest*), and may also have traveled and had contact with other scholars.

Life's Work

The scope of Alhazen's work is impressive. He wrote studies on mathema-

Triplicis uiſus, directi, reflexi & refracti, de quo optica diſputat, argumenta.

Frontispiece from Alhazen's *Optics*, 1572

tics, physics, astronomy, and medicine, as well as commentaries on the writings of Aristotle and Galen. He was an exact observer, a skilled experimenter, and an insightful theoretician, and he put these abilities to excellent use in the field of optics. He has been called the most important figure in optics between antiquity and the seventeenth century. Within optics itself, the range of his interests was wide: He discussed theories of light and vision, the anatomy and diseases of the eye, reflection and refraction, the rainbow, lenses, spherical and parabolic mirrors, and the pinhole camera (camera obscura).

Alhazen's most important work was *Kitāb al-Manāzir*, commonly known as *Optics*. Not published until 1572, and only appearing in the West in the Latin translation *Opticae thesaurus Alhazeni libri vii*, it attempted to clarify the subject by inquiring into its principles. He rejected Euclid's and Ptolemy's doctrine of visual rays (the extramission theory, which regarded vision as analogous to the sense of touch). For example, Ptolemy attributed sight to the action of visual rays issuing conically from the observer's eye and being reflected from various objects. Alhazen also disagreed with past versions of the intromission theory, which treated the visible object as a source from which forms (simulacra) issued. The atomists, for example, held that objects shed sets of atoms as a snake sheds its skin; when this set enters the eye, vision occurs. In another version of the intromission theory, Aristotle treated the visible object as a modifier of the medium between the object and the eye. Alhazen found the atomistic theory unconvincing because it could not explain how the image of a large mountain could enter the small pupil of the eye. He did not like the Aristotelian theory because it could not explain how the eye could distinguish individual parts of the seen world, since objects altered the entire intervening medium. Alhazen, in his version of the intromission theory, treated the visible object as a collection of small areas, each of which sends forth its own ray. He believed that vision takes place through light rays reflected from every point on an object's surface converging toward an apex in the eye.

According to Alhazen, light is an essential form in self-luminous bodies, such as the sun, and an accidental form in bodies that derive their luminosity from outside sources. Accidental light, such as the moon, is weaker than essential light, but both forms are emitted by their respective sources in exactly the same way: noninstantaneously, from every point on the source, in all directions, and along straight lines. To establish rectilinear propagation for essential, accidental, reflected, and refracted radiation, Alhazen performed many experiments with dark chambers, pinhole cameras, sighting tubes, and strings.

In the first book of *Optics*, Alhazen describes the anatomy of the eye. His description is not original, being based largely on the work of Galen, but he modifies traditional ocular geometry to suit his own explanation of vision.

For example, he claims that sight occurs in the eye by means of the glacial humor (what would be called the crystalline lens), because when this humor is injured, vision is destroyed. He also uses such observations as eye pain while gazing on intense light and afterimages from strongly illuminated objects to argue against the visual-ray theory, because these observations show that light is coming to the eye from the object. With this picture of intromission established, Alhazen faces the problem of explaining how replicas as big as a mountain can pass through the tiny pupil into the eye.

He begins the solution of this problem by recognizing that every point in the eye receives a ray from every point in the visual field. The difficulty with this punctiform analysis is that, if each point on the object sends light and color in every direction to each point of the eye, then all this radiation would arrive at the eye in total confusion; for example, colors would arrive mixed. Simply put, the problem is a superfluity of rays. To explain vision, each point of the surface of the glacial humor needs to receive a ray from only one point in the visual field. In short, it is necessary to establish a one-to-one correspondence between points in the visual field and points in the eye.

To fulfill this goal, Alhazen notices that only one ray from each point in the visual field falls perpendicularly on the convex surface of the eye. He then proposes that all other rays, those falling at oblique angles to the eye's surface, are refracted and so weakened that they are incapable of affecting visual power. Alhazen even performed an experiment to show that perpendicular rays are strong and oblique rays weak: He shot a metal sphere against a dish both perpendicularly and obliquely. The perpendicular shot fractured the plate, whereas the oblique shot bounced off harmlessly. Thus, in his theory, the cone of perpendicular rays coming into the eye accounts for the perception of the visible object's shape and the laws of perspective.

Book 2 of *Optics* contains Alhazen's theory of cognition based on visual perception, and book 3 deals with binocular vision and visual errors. Catoptrics (the theory of reflected light) is the subject of book 4. Alhazen here formulates the laws of reflection: Incident and reflected rays are in the same plane, and incident and reflected angles are equal. The equality of the angles of incidence and reflection allows Alhazen to explain the formation of an image in a plane mirror. As throughout *Optics*, Alhazen here uses experiments to help establish his contentions. For example, by throwing an iron sphere against a metal mirror at an oblique angle, he found that the incident and reflected movements of the sphere were symmetrical. The reflected movement of the iron sphere, because of its heaviness, did not continue in a straight line, as the light ray does, but Alhazen did not contend that the iron sphere is an exact duplicate of the light ray.

Alhazen's investigation of reflection continues in books 5 and 6 of *Optics*. Book 5 contains the famous "Problem of Alhazen": For any two points opposite a spherical reflecting surface, either convex or concave, find the point or points on the surface at which the light from one of the two points will be reflected to the other. Today it is known that the algebraic solution of this problem leads to an equation of the fourth degree, but Alhazen solved it geometrically by the intersection of a circle and a hyperbola.

Book 7, which concludes *Optics*, is devoted to dioptrics (the theory of refraction). Although Alhazen did not discover the mathematical relationship between the angles of incidence and refraction, his treatment of the phenomenon was the most extensive and enlightening before that of René Descartes. As with reflection, Alhazen explores refraction through a mechanical analogy. Light, he says, moves with great speed in a transparent medium such as air and with slower speed in a dense body such as glass or water. The slower speed of the light ray in the denser medium is the result of the greater resistance it encounters, but this resistance is not strong enough to hinder its movement completely. Since the refracted light ray is not strong enough to maintain its original direction in the denser medium, it moves in another direction along which its passage will be easier (that is, it turns toward the normal). This idea of the easier and quicker path was the basis of Alhazen's explanation of refraction, and it is a forerunner of the principle of least time associated with the name of Pierre de Fermat.

Optics was Alhazen's most significant work and by far his best known, but he also wrote more modest treatises in which he discussed the rainbow, shadows, camera obscura, and Ptolemy's optics as well as spheroidal and paraboloidal burning mirrors. The ancient Greeks had a good understanding of plane mirrors, but Alhazen developed an exhaustive geometrical analysis of the more difficult problem of the formation of images in spheroidal and paraboloidal mirrors.

Although Alhazen's achievements in astronomy do not equal those in optics, his extant works reveal his mastery of the techniques of Ptolemaic astronomy. These works are mostly short tracts on minor problems, for example, sundials, moonlight, eclipses, parallax, and determining the *gibla* (the direction to be faced in prayer). In another treatise, he was able to explain the apparent increase in size of heavenly bodies near the horizon, and he also estimated the thickness of the atmosphere.

His best astronomical work, and the only one known to the medieval West, was *Hay'at al-'alan* (tenth or eleventh century; on the configuration of the world). This treatise grew out of Alhazen's desire that the astronomical system should correspond to the true movements of actual heavenly bodies. He therefore attacked Ptolemy's system, in which the motions of heavenly bodies were explained in terms of imaginary points moving on imaginary circles. In his work, Alhazen tried to discover the physical reality underlying Ptolemy's abstract astronomical system. He accomplished this task by viewing the heavens as a series of concentric spherical shells whose rotations were interconnected. Alhazen's system accounted for the apparent motions of the heavenly bodies in a clear and untechnical way, which accounts for the book's popularity in the Middle Ages.

Alhazen's fame as a mathematician has largely depended on his geometrical solutions of various optical problems, but more than twenty strictly mathematical treatises have survived. Some of these deal with geometrical problems arising from his studies of Euclid's *Elements*, whereas others deal with quadrature problems, that is, constructing squares equal in area to various plane figures. He also wrote a work on lunes (figures contained between the arcs of two circles) and on the properties of conic sections. Although he was not successful with every problem, his performance, which exhibited his masterful command of higher mathematics, has rightly won for him the admiration of later mathematicians.

Summary

Alhazen was undoubtedly the greatest Muslim scientist, and *Optics* was the most important work in the field from Ptolemy's time to Johannes Kepler's. He extricated himself from the limitations of such earlier theories as the atomistic, Aristotelian, and Ptolemaic and integrated what he knew about medicine, physics, and mathematics into a single comprehensive theory of light and vision. Although his theory contained ideas from older theories, he combined these ideas with his new insights into a fresh creation, which became the source of a new optical tradition.

His optical theories had some influence on Islamic scientists, but their main impact was on the West. *Optics* was translated from Arabic into Latin at the end of the twelfth century. It was widely studied, and in the thirteenth century, Witelo (also known as Vitellio) made liberal use of Alhazen's text in writing his comprehensive book on optics. Roger Bacon, John Peckham, and Giambattista della Porta are only some of the many thinkers who were influenced by Alhazen's work. Indeed, it was not until Kepler, six centuries later, that work on optics progressed beyond the point to which Alhazen had brought it. Even Kepler, however, used some of Alhazen's ideas, for example, the one-to-one correspondence between points on the object and points in the eye. It would not be going too far to say that Alhazen's optical theories defined the scope and goals of the field from his day to ours.

Bibliography

Grant, Edward, ed. *A Source Book in Medieval Science*. Cambridge, Mass.: Harvard University Press, 1974. A compilation of readings from medieval natural philosophers, including several selections in English translation from the works of Alhazen.

Hayes, John Richard, ed. *The Genius of Arab Civilization: Source of Renaissance*. Cambridge, Mass.: MIT Press, 1978. In this beautifully illustrated book, several international authorities discuss the achievements of

Islamic culture. Abdelhamid I. Sabra's chapter on the exact sciences contains an account of Alhazen's work in the context of Islamic intellectual history. Includes indexes and a bibliography.

Lindberg, David C. *Theories of Vision from al-Kindi to Kepler*. Chicago: University of Chicago Press, 1976. Lindberg surveys visual theory against the background of ancient accomplishments. His chapter on Alhazen's intromission theory is excellent.

__________, ed. *Science in the Middle Ages*. Chicago: University of Chicago Press, 1978. Through the expertise of several historians of medieval science, this book examines in depth all major aspects of natural philosophy in the Middle Ages. The approach is not encyclopedic but interpretative. Lindberg is the author of the chapter on optics, in which Alhazen's work is clearly explained.

Nasr, Seyyed Hossein. *Islamic Science: An Illustrated Study*. Westerham, England: World of Islam Festival Publishing Co., 1976. The first illustrated study ever undertaken of the whole of Islamic science. Using traditional Islamic concepts, Nasr discusses various branches of science, including optics.

__________. *Science and Civilization in Islam*. Cambridge, Mass.: Harvard University Press, 1968. This book is the first one-volume work in English to deal with Islamic science from the Muslim rather than the Western viewpoint. Its approach is encyclopedic rather than analytic, but it does contain a discussion of Alhazen's work in its Muslim context.

Sabra, Abdelhamid I. *Theories of Light from Descartes to Newton*. London: Oldbourne Book Co., 1967. Though this book is mainly centered on seventeenth century theories of light, Sabra discusses in detail the impact of Alhazen's ideas on the optical discoveries of such men as Descartes and Christiaan Huygens.

Robert J. Paradowski

VIKTOR A. AMBARTSUMIAN

Born: September 18; 1908; Tiflis, Russia

Area of Achievement: Astronomy
Contribution: Ambartsumian developed the astrophysics of stars and stellar origins and was instrumental in the theory of gigantic catastrophe formation in galaxies related to the evolution of stars and galaxies. He was the founder of the major school of theoretical astrophysics in the U.S.S.R.

Early Life

Very few biographical details of Viktor A. Ambartsumian's childhood are known. He was born in 1908, in Tiflis, Russia (modern Tbilisi, U.S.S.R.), the son of a local teacher of literature. Early in school, he developed a passion for mathematics and physics and became extremely interested in the formation, evolution, and energy generation of stars and other heavenly bodies. Following his instincts, he went to the University of Leningrad, from which he was graduated in 1928 with high honors. He performed so well and so amazed his instructors that he was offered a position at the university, where he stayed to teach until 1944. In that year, he went to Yerevan, Soviet Armenia, to become the founder and director of the Byurakan Observatory and its subsequent permanent director.

Life's Work

Very early in his career at the Byurakan Observatory, Ambartsumian became interested in the physics of stars and nebulas, combined with a general regard for astronomical topics of all characteristics. As a by-product of his work, he became the founder of the school for theoretical astrophysics in the U.S.S.R., concentrating much of his time and effort on the cosmogony of stars and galaxies. It was his detailed work on the theory of stellar origins that brought him early recognition, particularly his explanation, derived by both reasoning and mathematics, of how gigantic catastrophic explosions had taken place elsewhere in the universe and how such explosions could take place in, or even be required for, the evolution of stars and galaxies. The idea originated from the work of Walter Baade and Hermann Minkowski, who first identified a radio source of extraordinary violence in the constellation of Cygnus. Baade had first announced that the radio source was associated with what appeared to be a closely connected pair of distant galaxies. In the photographs, it appeared that a gigantic collision was occurring, a supremely colossal event that could account for the extensive radio spectrum being emitted from that particular region of extragalactic space. Baade believed that events such as this catastrophe might even be common enough in the universe to account for the numerous extragalactic radio

Library of Congress

sources already identified by that time. Ambartsumian, however, in 1955 was able to gather enough evidence, both observational and theoretical, to show that the collision view was undoubtedly wrong. As an alternative, he proposed that vast explosions could occur within the core of a galaxy, creating a tremendous release of energy, somewhat analogous to supernova explosions, only on a galactic, rather than a stellar, scale. Mechanisms for such titanic explosions include chain-reaction supernovas erupting in the densely packed galactic core, interactions of normal matter and antimatter, the possible interactions of stars and interstellar materials with a superheavy black hole, or the total destruction of a galaxy's nucleus through some other mechanism involving fantastic releases of energy, much more than could ever be derived from simple atom bomb explosions. The discovery of other galaxies (particularly that by Allan Sandage, who worked with M-82) in the process of definitely exploding has led to Ambartsumian's hypothesis' becoming well established in current astrophysical thought.

In his role as founder of the Soviet school of combined theoretical physics and astronomy, Ambartsumian initiated the study of numerous topics, in some areas virtually inventing, redefining, and mathematically settling the field. He founded the quantitative theory for emissions of light energy from gaseous nebulas, a precursor to his ideas on how stars formed. As a method for forming such gaseous nebulas, he established a detailed synthesis for calculating the masses ejected by stars in their normal, nonstationary state, now called solar wind, and for those far enough along in their life history to become novas or exploding stars. To handle large groups of stars, such as those found in globular clusters of up to one million members, Ambartsumian developed the fundamentals of statistical mechanics as applied to stellar systems. One of the offshoots of that work was his ability to demonstrate that smaller stellar clusters, such as galactic open-star clusters, gradually decay via the loss of individual stars. On that basis, he found he could estimate the ages of the observable clusters in our galaxy.

While working as a scientist, he also performed other functions. From a role as a corresponding member in 1939, he became an academician of the Academy of Sciences of the U.S.S.R. in 1953, supplementing the position he had already held since 1943 as academician of the Academy of Sciences of Soviet Armenia. He was president of that group in 1947. Also in 1947, he became a professor at the University of Yerevan.

In the late 1940's, Ambartsumian became proficient in dealing with some fundamental problems of stellar cosmogony. In 1947, he had discovered dynamically unstable systems of a new type, called stellar associations. By studying these extremely young collections of stars, he found that light, traveling through supposedly empty space, was not being absorbed by a continuous distribution of matter in the interstellar space but rather was reduced principally by discrete dark nebulas lying between stars and the observer. He formulated a special mathematical theory for statistical research on these peculiar interstellar absorption dustballs, in the process solving numerous problems with a theory of light-scattering in dense, turbid media. His work saw the formation of stars as collapsing clouds of dust under gravity forming embryonic stars fueled by the infalling hydrogen from the dark nebula surrounding the stellar nursery. A special case he developed was the theory of baryonic stars, stars possessing a density much greater than nuclear density, which was a forerunner of the black hole idea.

Ambartsumian also had a substantial influence on the trend of dealing with the enormous activity found in central galactic areas. He proved that the nuclei of galaxies were indeed responsible for a host of recently discovered phenomena, including colossal explosions greater than anything ever before perceived, ejections of fantastic quantities of materials by both violent and quiescent means, and extremely intense emissions of radio waves, microwaves, and gamma radiation. Ambartsumian's treatment of these matters has had an impact on the new astronomy that uses the entire electromagnetic spectrum for surveying the universe.

Ambartsumian has acted as both vice president (1948-1955) and president (1961-1964) of the International Astronomical Union. He has also been a member of many different foreign academies and scientific societies. In 1968, he was elected president of the International Council of Scientific Unions. He was twice awarded the State Prize of the U.S.S.R., in 1946 and 1950, has been awarded the Order of Lenin on three separate occasions, and has received numerous other orders and medals, both within the U.S.S.R. and from foreign scientific societies.

Summary

Viktor A. Ambartsumian was one of the most visible Soviet astronomers through the early 1980's, primarily because of his frequent attendance at numerous international scientific meetings. Although he acted as member and president of the Armenian Academy of Sciences, and, since 1953, has been a member of the U.S.S.R. Academy of Sciences as a theoretical astrophysicist, he has also been an aggressive supporter of observational astronomy. Under his directorship, the Byurakan Observatory has risen to the forefront of the astronomical facilities in the Soviet Union. He has led the push to develop vast areas of astronomical research in the Soviet Union, including planetary astronomy (particularly studies of Venus), meteorites, and comets; a second major program on stellar astronomy, particularly stellar associations, flare stars, symbiotic stars, and normal stellar phenomena; and, finally, extragalactic astronomy, particularly those Markarian galaxies bright in ultraviolet light, active galaxies, and theoretical galactic studies.

Ambartsumian has been a professor at the University of Yerevan since 1947. He became a Hero of Socialist Labor in 1968 for his many contributions in science and government. He has particularly enjoyed giving public lectures, extolling an all-union society, Znanya (knowledge), which connects many outstanding scholars with adult education and helps shape policy on the numerous planetariums in the country. He is strongly in favor of the many flourishing academies established throughout the U.S.S.R. which have helped to revive the culture of particular nationalities. He has not seen this mixing of astronomy and government as a problem; rather, he sees both areas as part of his own personal search for a succinct view of the universe.

Bibliography

Asimov, Isaac. *The Exploding Suns: The Secrets of the Supernovas.* New York: E. P. Dutton, 1985. A delightful exploration of the life history of stars, emphasizing their origins and their ultimate fates as bodies destined to explode. Follows the history of various size stars to their ends as planetary nebulas, novas, or supernovas. This book is excellent reading. Well illustrated and designed for the layperson.

Mihalas, Dmitri, with Paul McRae Routly. *Galactic Astronomy.* San Francisco: W. H. Freeman, 1968. Deals with all the configurations of a normal galaxy, from stars and their origins to the gaseous contents found between the stars. Traces the evolution of stars and star clusters and discusses energy generation near galactic cores. Heavy reading with an extensive bibliography for references and some mathematics.

Murdin, Paul. *The New Astronomy.* New York: Thomas Y. Crowell, 1978. Written for the layperson, this work deals with the end of stellar evolution, when the catastrophic collapses occur. Tracing the trail of ancient supernovas, the story of the creation of the elements, black holes, and neutron stars is told, ending with the ultimate fate of the universe. Contains line diagrams.

Reddish, V. C. *Stellar Formation.* Elmsford, N.Y.: Pergamon Press, 1978. A detailed account of how stars form from the condensation of dust and gases found in the nebulas of the galaxy. The evidence for stellar birth is presented clearly, and subsequent evolution is presented in enough detail to show the resultant stages of life for different-sized bodies. Includes extensive mathematics and extra references. College-level physics is necessary for complete understanding.

Shklovskii, I. *Stars: Their Birth, Life, and Death.* San Francisco: W. H. Freeman, 1978. For the advanced layperson, an excellent summary detailing the origin of stars from dust clouds, their subsequent evolution through middle age, and their ultimate demise based on their original size. Clearly illustrated, with extensive references. Some mathematics.

Zeilik, Michael, ed. *Cool Stars, Stellar Systems, and the Sun.* London: Springer-Verlag, 1986. A collection of articles presented on star systems under various conditions of size, temperature, and activity. The evolution of lower-temperature stars is discussed, as are the life features of multiple-star collections. The sun's history is used for comparison. Contains extensive references and heavy mathematics.

Zeldovich, Ya. B., and I. D. Novikov. *Stars and Relativity.* Vol. 1. Chicago: University of Chicago Press, 1971. A detailed treatise on the history of stars from their birth to their ultimate evolutionary stage, based on information predicted by the theory of relativity. Deals with exploding bodies, interactions of stars within galaxies, and catastrophes in nature. Extremely detailed in mathematics but possesses a tremendous amount of information.

Arthur L. Alt

ANAXAGORAS

Born: c. 500 B.C.; Clazomenae, Anatolia
Died: c. 428 B.C.; Lampsacus
Areas of Achievement: Philosophy, natural history, and science
Contribution: By devising a philosophical system to explain the origins and nature of the physical universe which overcame the paradoxes and inconsistencies of earlier systems, Anaxagoras provided an indispensable bridge between the pre-Socratic philosophers of the archaic period of Greek history and the full flowering of philosophy during the Golden Age of Greece.

Early Life

Virtually nothing is known of Anaxagoras' parents, his childhood, his adolescence, or his education. Born into a wealthy family in an Ionian Greek city, he almost certainly was exposed to the attempts by Ionian philosophers, especially Parmenides, to explain the physical universe by postulating that everything is made from a single primordial substance. Anaxagoras apparently realized even before he was twenty years of age that such an assumption could not explain the phenomena of movement and change, and he began to devise a more satisfactory system.

He grew to adulthood during the turbulent years of the wars of the Greek city-states against the Persian Empire. His own city, Clazomenae, forced to acknowledge the suzerainty of Darius the Great in 514, joined the Athenian-aided Ionian revolt against Persia in 498. That revolt was ultimately suppressed in 493. Anaxagoras' childhood was spent during a time when the echoes of Athens' great victory over Darius at Marathon in 490 were reverberating throughout the Hellenic world.

According to tradition, Anaxagoras became a resident of Athens in 480. That a young scholar should be attracted to the intellectual and artistic center of Greek civilization is not surprising, but it is doubtful that this change of residence took place in 480. Xerxes I chose that year to attempt to realize Darius' dream of conquering the Greek polis. His plans were frustrated and his great host scattered at the battles of Salamis and Plataea during that same year. The next year, the Ionian cities of Asia Minor again rose in rebellion against Persia, and in 477, joined with Athens in the Delian League. The League succeeded in expelling the Persians from the Greek states of Asia Minor. It seems more likely that the young Anaxagoras came to Athens after the alliance between the Ionian cities and the Athenians.

While in Athens, Anaxagoras became friends with the young Pericles and apparently influenced him considerably. Several classical scholars have concluded that Anaxagoras' later trial was engineered by Pericles' political rivals, in order to deprive Pericles of a trusted friend. Convicted of impiety

Ann Ronan Picture Library

after admitting that he thought the sun was a huge mass of "hot rock," Anaxagoras went into exile at Lampsacus, where many young Greeks came to study with him before his death, probably in 428.

Life's Work

Sometime in or shortly after 467, Anaxagoras published his only written work, apparently entitled *Nature*. Of this work, only seventeen fragments totaling around twelve hundred words have survived, all recorded as quotations in the works of later generations of philosophers. That so few words could have inspired the more than fifty books and articles written about him in the twentieth century alone is ample testimony to Anaxagoras' importance in the evolution of Greek philosophy and natural science.

Anaxagoras' book was an ambitious attempt to explain the origins and nature of the universe without recourse (or so it seemed to many of his contemporaries) to any supernatural agents. Other Ionian philosophers, notably Parmenides, had preceded Anaxagoras in this endeavor, but their systems were logically unable to explain the multiplicity of "things" in the universe or to explain physical and biological change in those things because they had postulated that all things are made from the same basic "stuff." Anaxagoras overcame the logical inconsistencies of this argument by postulating an infinite variety of substances that make up the whole of the universe. Anaxagoras argued that there is something of everything in everything. By this he meant that, for example, water contains a part of every other thing in the universe, from blood to rock to air. The reason that it is perceived to be water is that most of its parts are water. A hair also contains parts of every other thing, but most of its parts are hair.

In the beginning, according to the first fragment of Anaxagoras' book, infinitely small parts of everything in equal proportions were together in a sort of primal soup. In fragment 3, he proposes a primitive version of the law of the conservation of energy, by saying that anything, no matter how small, can be divided infinitely, because it is not possible for something to become nonexistent through dividing. This idea of infinite divisibility is unique to the Anaxagorean system; no philosopher before or since has proposed it.

This universal mixture of all things acquired form and substance, according to fragment 12, through the actions of *nous*, or "Mind." Mind, Anaxagoras argues, is not part of everything (though it is a part of some things), nor is a part of everything found in Mind (though parts of some things are found in Mind). Mind set the primal soup into rotation and the different things began to "separate off," thus forming the universe. The rotation of the primal mixture not only separated everything according to its kind (but not perfectly, since everything still contains parts of every other thing) but also supplied heat, through friction. Among other things, friction ignited the sun and the stars. Considerable disagreement over the exact meaning Anaxagoras was trying to convey with the term "Mind" has colored scholarly works on his book since Aristotle and continues to be a controversial issue.

Anaxagoras' system not only enabled him and his students to describe all existing objects, but it also permitted the explanation of physical and biological change. It was the introduction of the idea of Mind and its action as a formative agent in the creation of the universe for which Anaxagoras became famous and which rejuvenated Socrates' interest and faith in philosophy.

Sometime after 467, Anaxagoras was accused of and tried for impiety (denying the gods) and "medism" (sympathizing with the Persians). The actual date of his trial and subsequent banishment from Athens is still hotly debated among classical scholars. The traditional date accepted by most historians is 450, but this seems unlikely for several reasons. By 450, the charge of medism could hardly have been a serious one, since the Persian wars were long since over. Also, had he been in Athens in 450, the young Socrates would almost certainly have met him personally, but Socrates' own words indicate that he knew Anaxagoras only through his book. Finally, Anaxagoras' friend Pericles would have been fully able to protect his mentor from political opponents in 450. An earlier date for his exile from Athens seems likely. Some scholars have attempted to solve this problem by postulating that Anaxagoras visited Athens one or more times after being exiled shortly after the publication of his book. This seems the most reasonable explanation to reconcile the dispute, especially since several ancient sources place him in Athens as late as 437.

One of Anaxagoras' most notable achievements during his stay in Athens was to postulate the correct explanation for a solar eclipse. Anaxagoras was apparently the first to argue that an eclipse occurs when the moon (which he said was a large mass of cold rocks) passes between the Earth and the sun (which he said was a larger mass of hot rocks). He may have reached this conclusion after the fall of a large meteorite near Aegypotomi in 467, which excited wide discussion throughout the Hellenic world.

After leaving Athens, Anaxagoras spent his remaining years as the head of a flourishing school at Lampsacus. How his philosophical system may have changed over the years between the publication of his book and the end of his life is unknown. He died at Lampsacus, probably in 428.

Summary

The thesis that Anaxagoras greatly influenced Socrates and Aristotle is easily proved by their elaborate discussions of his system in their own words. Through those two most influential of all Greek thinkers, he has had a profound impact on all subsequent generations of philosophers and natural scientists in the Western world. Some of Anaxagoras' critics, both ancient and modern, accuse him of merely substituting the word "Mind" for "God," or "the gods." Thus in their estimation his philosophy becomes merely a humanistic religion. Other critics have dismissed Anaxagoras' teachings as simplistic and unworthy of serious consideration. His supporters, from Aristotle to the present, have defended him as a pioneering thinker who provided much of the inspiration for the flowering of post-Socratic philosophy during the Golden Age of Greece and the Hellenistic world.

Early critics and supporters alike may have missed an important point in the Anaxagoras fragments. Late twentieth century work on Anaxagoras points out that his concept of Mind giving form to the universe is not far removed from the position of some modern physicists who argue that our perception of the universe is determined by our own senses, which provide an imperfect understanding at best. Anaxagoras may well have been trying to express this same concept (that without cognitive perception there is no form or substance to the universe) without possessing the technical language to do so.

Bibliography

Davison, J. A."Protagoras, Democritus, and Anaxagoras." *Classical Quarterly*, N.s. 3 (1953): 33-45. Establishes Anaxagoras' position vis-à-vis other Greek philosophers and shows his influence on the "atomist" school that succeeded him. Also contains some information on his early life not available elsewhere in English and argues for an early date for his exile from Athens.

Gershenson, Daniel E., and Daniel A. Greenberg. *Anaxagoras and the Birth of Physics*. New York: Blaisdell Publishing Co., 1964. This controversial work suggests that the Anaxagoras fragments are not really the words of Anaxagoras, but rather his words as interpreted by later philosophers, notably Simplicius, who succeeded him. Contains a good, if somewhat theoretical, explanation of Anaxagoras' system.

Guthrie, W. K. C. *A History of Greek Philosophy*. Vol. 2. Cambridge: Cambridge University Press, 1965. Contains the most complete account available of Anaxagoras' life. Puts his life and teachings in the context of his times.

Kirk, G. S., and J. E. Raven. *The Presocratic Philosophers: A Critical History with a Selection of Texts*. Cambridge: Cambridge University Press, 1957. A very readable account of Anaxagoras' life and works and of his place in the history of philosophy.

Mansfield, J. "The Chronology of Anaxagoras' Athenian Period and the Date of His Trial." *Mnemosyne* 33 (1980): 17-95. Offers the most convincing arguments concerning Anaxagoras' arrival in Athens, his trial, and his banishment. Also contains references to Anaxagoras' relationship with Pericles and the political motives behind the former's exile.

Schofield, Malcolm. *An Essay on Anaxagoras*. Cambridge: Cambridge University Press, 1980. A clear, witty exposition of the philosophy of Anaxagoras and his importance in the history of philosophy. Perhaps the best work on Anaxagoras' system and its meaning available in English.

Taylor, A. E. "On the Date of the Trial of Anaxagoras." *Classical Quarterly* 11 (1917): 81-87. A good discussion of the backdrop against which Anaxagoras' sojourn in Athens was played and the political and intellectual milieu during which his book was written.

Teodorsson, Sven-Tage. *Anaxagoras' Theory of Matter*. Göteborg, Sweden: Acta Universitatis Gothoburgensis, 1982. Although this book is too difficult for the average reader (its author includes quotations throughout the text in six different languages), it is valuable because it contains the best English translation of the Anaxagoras fragments.

Paul Madden

ANAXIMANDER

Born: c. 610 B.C.; Miletus, Greek Asia Minor
Died: c. 547 B.C.; probably Miletus
Areas of Achievement: Natural history, astronomy, and geography
Contribution: Anaximander realized that no ordinary physical element could be the source of the world's diversity; instead, he saw that the fundamental stuff must be an eternal, unlimited reservoir of qualities and change.

Early Life

Anaximander was a fellow citizen and student of Thales, the Milesian usually credited with having inaugurated Western philosophy. Thales, some forty years older than his protégé, put none of his philosophical thought in writing and maintained no formal pedagogical associations with pupils. Yet Thales' cosmological views (as reconstructed by historians) doubtless inspired Anaximander, and Anaximander finally expanded on Thales' ideas with innovative leaps in conceptual abstraction.

Anaximander was known in his day for his practical achievements and his astronomical discoveries. Anaximander is said to have been chosen by the Milesians as the leader for a new colony in Apollonia on the Black Sea. He traveled widely and was the first Greek to publish a "geographical tablet," a map of the world. The map was circular, and it was centered on the city of Delphi, since Delphi was the location of the *omphalos*, or "navel" stone, that was thought to be the center of Earth. Anaximander is also said to have designed a celestial map and to have specified the proportions of stellar orbits. In addition to the celestial map, he built a spherical model of the stars and planets, with Earth located at the center and represented as a disk or cylinder whose height was one third its diameter. The heavenly bodies were rings of hollow pipe of different sizes that were placed on circling wheels in ratios of three to six to nine, in proportion to the magnitude of Earth. This model was dynamic; the wheels could be moved at different speeds, making it possible to visualize patterns of planetary motion. Anaximander is also credited with inventing the sundial, or gnomon, and with having discovered the zodiac.

All these eclectic interests and discoveries illustrate, with elegance, Anaximander's particular genius, namely, his rational view of the world. This way of thinking was quite an innovation at a time when both scientific and protophilosophical thought took their content from the mythical and literary traditions, and thus were marked by vagueness and mystery. Anaximander viewed the world as steadily legible; he had the expectation of its rational intelligibility. His map of the world and his model of the heavens show his anticipation of symmetry and order. Earth, he argued, remained at rest in the center of the cosmos by reason of its equidistance at all points to the celestial circum-

ference; it had no reason to be pulled in one direction in preference to any other. He projected the celestial orbits in perfect and pleasing proportions, and he anticipated regular motions.

Anaximander's mapping and modeling techniques themselves were products of his rationalistic thinking. Models and maps relocate some set of unified phenomena into a new level of abstraction. Implicit in map and model design is the assumption that the abstractions will preserve the intelligible relationships present in the world that they reproduce. Thus Anaximander's introduction of models and maps represents a tremendous and utterly original conceptual leap from the world "seen" to the world's operations understood and faithfully reproduced by the abstracting human mind.

Life's Work

Anaximander's rational view of the world received its fullest and most innovative expression in his philosophy of nature. Here one finds the first unified and all-encompassing picture of the world of human experience in history that is based on rational deduction and explanation of all phenomena.

In order to understand Anaximander properly, his terminology must be put into its historical context. What Anaximander (and Thales as well) understood by "nature" is not quite the same as its modern sense. In Ionian Greece, *physis* denoted the process of growth and emergence. It also denoted something's origin, or source, that from which the thing is constantly renewed. Nature, in the Ionian sense of *physis*, had nothing to do with matter; even Aristotle was mistaken in thinking that it did. In fact, no word for matter even existed in Anaximander's day. It is also important to note that Anaximander's thought is reconstructed entirely from ancient secondary sources. The one extant fragment of Anaximander's own words is the quotation of an ancient historian. Thus, any explication of Anaximander's thought is to some extent conjectural and interpretive.

Anaximander's philosophy of nature arose in part as a response to Thales' ideas on nature. Thales held that Water was the nature of everything. This meant, in the light of the ancient idea of *physis*, that Water was the origin of everything, that everything was sustained by, and constantly renewed from, Water. This notion does not have any allegorical or mythical connotations in Thales' formulation. Water is the ordinary physical stuff in the world, not some engendering god such as the Oceanus of Thales' predecessors. That is the reason Thales is the first philosopher: He had a theory about the origin of things that competed with ancient creation myths.

Anaximander agreed with Thales that the origin of the things of the world was some common stuff, but he thought that the stuff could not be some ordinary element. He rejected Thales' conception on purely logical grounds, and his reasoning was quite interesting. How could any manifestly singular stuff ever give rise to qualities that pertained to things differently constituted, such as earth and fire? What is more, if Water were the source of things, would not drying destroy them? Thus, reasoned Anaximander, the thing with which the world begins cannot be identical with any of the ordinary stuff with which humans are acquainted, but it must be capable of giving rise to the wide multiplicity of things and their pairs of contrary qualities. What therefore distinguishes the source from the world is that the source itself is "unbounded": It can have no definite shape or quality of its own but must be a reservoir from which every sort or characteristic in the world may be spawned. So Anaximander called the source of things this very name: *apeiron*, Boundlessness, or the Boundless. Anaximander designated the Boundless an *arche*, a beginning, but he did not mean a temporal beginning. The Boundless can have no beginning, nor can it pass away, for it can have no bounds, including temporal ones.

Thus the eternal source, the Boundless, functions as a storehouse of the world's qualities, such that the qualities that constitute some present state of the world have been separated out of the stock, and when their contrary qualities become manifest, they will, in turn, be reabsorbed into the reservoir. When Earth is hot, heat will come forth from the Boundless; when Earth cools, cold will come forth and heat will go back. For Anaximander, this process continued in never-ending cycles.

The cause of the alternating manifestations of contrary qualities is the subject of the single existing fragment of Anaximander's own words, the only remains of the first philosophy ever written. Out of the Boundless, Anaximander explains, the worlds arise, but

> from whatever things is the genesis of the things that are, into these they must pass away according to necessity; for they must pay the penalty and make atonement to one another for their injustice according to the ordering of Time.

History has produced no consensus of interpretation for this passage and its picturesque philosophical metaphor for the rationale of the world. Anaximander was probably thinking of a courtroom image. Each existing thing is in a state of "having-too-much," so that during the time it exists it "commits injustice" against its opposite by preventing it from existing. In retribution, the existing thing must cede its overt existence for its opposite to enjoy and pay the penalty of returning to the submerged place in the great Boundless reservoir. This cycling, he added, is how Time is ordered or measured. Time is the change, the alternating manifestation of opposites.

Here is the apotheosis of Anaximander's rational worldview. The world's workings are not simply visible and perspicuous, but neither are they whimsical and mysterious. The hidden workings of things may be revealed in the abstractions of the human mind. The world works, and is the way that it is, according to an eternal and intelligible principle. What is more, this world and its workings are unified, indeed form a cosmos. The cosmos, in turn, can be understood and explained by analogy with the human world; the justice sought in the city's courts is the same justice that sustains everything that human perception finds in the universe.

Summary

Classical antiquity credited Thales with having pioneered philosophy. Anaximander, with his scientific curiosity and his genius for abstract insight, poised philosophical inquiry for new vistas of exploration; his new philosophical approach inaugurated penetrating, objective analysis. His principle of the eternal Boundless as the source of the world's multifarious qualities and change forms the conceptual backdrop against which twenty-five centuries of science and natural philosophy have developed.

Two particular innovations of Anaximander have never been abandoned. First, his extension of the concept of law from human society to the physical world continues to dictate the scientific worldview. The received view in Anaximander's time—that nature was capricious and anarchic—has never again taken hold. Second, Anaximander's invention of the use of models and maps revolutionized science and navigation and continues to be indispensable, even in people's daily lives. All scientific experiments are models of a sort: They are laboratory-scale contrivances of events or circumstances in the world at large. Purely visual three-dimensional models continue to be crucial in scientific discoveries: the so-called Bohr model of the atom played a crucial role in physics; the double-helical model was important to the discovery of the structure and function of DNA. Maps are taken for granted now, but if human beings had relied on verbal descriptions of spatial localities, civilization would not have proceeded very far.

Thus, Anaximander's innovations and influence persist. Indeed, it is difficult to imagine a world without his contributions. Anaximander himself could hardly have seen all the implications of his discoveries, for even now one can only guess at the future direction of abstract thought.

Bibliography

Brumbaugh, Robert S. *The Philosophers of Greece*. New York: Thomas Y. Crowell, 1964. This volume contains a short, digested chapter on Anaximander's life and accomplishments. Emphasizes cartography and engineering. Includes a reproduction of the first map designed by Anaximander.

Burnet, John. *Early Greek Philosophy*. 4th ed. New York: Barnes and Noble Books, 1945. A detailed scholarly analysis of Anaximander's thought in the context of comparisons with, and influences on, other pre-Socratic philosophers.

Guthrie, W. K. C. *A History of Greek Philosophy*. Vol. 1, *The Earlier Presocratics and the Pythagoreans*. Cambridge: Cambridge University

Press, 1962. Contains a chapter on Anaximander's cosmology. Focuses in a very close analysis on the concepts of *apeiron* and *apeiron* as *arche*.

Kahn, Charles H. *Anaximander and the Origins of Greek Cosmology*. New York: Columbia University Press, 1960. Surveys the documentary evidence for Anaximander's views, reconstructs a detailed cosmology from documentary texts, and devotes an entire chapter to analysis and interpretation of Anaximander's fragment.

Kirk, Geoffrey S., and John E. Raven. *The Presocratic Philosophers*. Cambridge: Cambridge University Press, 1957. Contains a chapter on Anaximander and a close formal analysis of textual testimony on Anaximander's thought.

Seligman, Paul. *The "Apeiron" of Anaximander*. London: Athlone Press, 1962. A detailed analysis of the *apeiron* as a linguistic concept and as a metaphysical entity.

Wheelwright, Philip, ed. *The Presocratics*. New York: Macmillan, 1966. A primary source. Contains the Anaximander fragment in translation. Also contains testimonies from Aristotle and other Greek and Latin sources who read and commented on Anaximander's treatise.

Patricia Cook

ANAXIMENES OF MILETUS

Born: Early sixth century B.C.; probably Miletus
Died: Second half of the sixth century B.C.; place unknown
Areas of Achievement: Philosophy and science
Contribution: Anaximenes was the last of the great early pre-Socratic thinkers from Miletus and the first, apparently, to attribute the nature of matter entirely to physical rather than moral laws. Thus, his ideas provided a necessary step from the generalized ideas of Thales to the specific physical ideas of the Atomists of the fifth century.

Early Life

The writings of Anaximenes of Miletus no longer exist. Thus, knowledge of Anaximenes is based on a few statements made by Aristotle and later writers on the history of Greek philosophy, some of whom quote earlier writers whose work is now lost. A few of these earlier writers show that they had access to Anaximenes' writings, but it is difficult to determine the veracity of any of their statements. Thus, scholars have almost no reliable information about Anaximenes' life; not even his dates can be accurately ascertained, and only the most general of assumptions can be made. These biographical assumptions are usually applied to Thales and Anaximander as well as Anaximenes. These men were the most famous thinkers from Miletus, then the largest and most prosperous Greek city on the west coast of Asia Minor.

While they are known only for their philosophical work, it is believed that all three were financially secure and that philosophical thought was for them an avocation. Apparently, Anaximenes was the youngest of the three. Some sources suggest that Anaximenes was the pupil of Anaximander, while others suggest that he was a fellow student and friend. Most scholars place the work of Anaximenes after the fall of Sardis to Cyrus the Great (c. 545 B.C.) and before the fall of Miletus (494 B.C.).

Life's Work

Anaximenes' work must be viewed against the background of sixth century Miletus and the work of his predecessors. Miletus in the sixth century was a flourishing center between the eastern kingdoms and the mainland of Greece. The city was ruled by a ruthless tyrant, Thrasybulus, whose methods of control were to do away with anyone who looked threatening.

It has been suggested that the emergence of tyranny in Miletus was the crucial factor in the emergence of philosophy, that the need to overthrow the existing myth-centered system of values was behind philosophical speculation. It has also been said that the emergence of philosophy coincides with the emergence of participatory forms of government, the development of written codes of law, and the expansion of the role of nonaristocrats in gov-

ernment through oratory, which encouraged logical argument and objective reasoning. As attractive as these theories may be, they overlook the fact that Miletus itself was under the rule of a tyrant who discouraged participatory democracy absolutely.

It seems more logical to conclude that philosophy became a means of escaping the brutality of the immediate, political world. Travel brought Milesians in contact with Egypt and Phoenicia—and eventually Mesopotamia. Milesians developed an independence of thought that led them to use their knowledge of the pragmatic world gained through observation to see the contradictions in the mythologies of different peoples and to make the leap to a nonmythologaical explanation of causation and the nature of matter.

The work of Anaximenes was summarized in a single book whose title is unknown. In the fourth century, Theophrastus, Aristotle's successor, is said to have noted its "simple and economical Ionic style." One supposes that this comment refers to the shift from writing in poetry to writing in prose. Clearly, Anaximenes was more concerned with content than with the conventions of poetical expression.

Anaximenes wrote that "air" was the original substance of matter. Scholars of ancient history agree, however, that the exact meaning of this statement is unclear. To take the position that all other matter was derived from air, Anaximenes must have believed that air was a changeable substance which, by rarefaction and condensation, was able to take other forms. When rarefied, it became fire; when condensed, it became wind, clouds, water, earth, and finally stones. Thus, Anaximenes had modified Thales' idea that water was the original substance and contradicted Anaximander's thesis of unchanging infinity while still staying within the Milesian monist tradition.

Having determined the nature of air and its properties, Anaximenes apparently developed other ideas by extension. Topics which he addressed include the nature of hot and cold as expressions of rarefaction and condensation, the divine nature of air, the motion of air, cosmogony, and cosmological problems. Under the latter heading he seems to have commented on the nature of Earth, which he saw as flat and riding on a cushion of air, and the nature of heavenly bodies. In his consideration of meteorological phenomena, Anaximenes seems to have followed Anaximander rather closely. Anaximenes' description of air also resembles Hesiod's description of Chaos. Both Chaos and air surround Earth, persist within the developed world, and can be characterized by darkness, internal motion, divinity, immense size, and probable homogeneity.

Anaximenes, like his two predecessors, challenged the mythological world of Homer and Hesiod by introducing free and rational speculation. Anaximenes also presented a challenge by writing in prose. Prior to this, poetry had been the perferred form for serious expression—not only in literature but also in politics. By writing in prose, the early philosophers moved, in part, from the world of the aristocrat to that of the new man of Greece: the hoplite, the merchant, the small, free farmer. While this new method of thought was not accepted by the average Greek (nor even, one suspects, the average Milesian), it did gain respect and placed philosophical speculation on an elevated footing.

For Anaximenes, unlike his predecessors, however, the differences that could be observed in matter were not qualitative but quantitative. Thus it is that he was the first to suggest a consistent picture of the world as a mechanism.

Summary

Any account of Anaximenes' life and ideas must by virtue of scant evidence be unsatisfactory. Yet in spite of a lack of information about him and his ideas, his place in and contribution to intellectual development are clear. Anaximenes' methods were far more influential than his specific theories on matter. Together with Thales and Anaximander, he was the first to free speculative thought from mythology and mythological terms. The methods of these three thinkers are the foundation for all modern scientific and philosophical thought. They began with intellectual curiosity about the nature of matter and combined this curiosity with keen observation of the world around them—with little regard to prior religious explanations.

At first glance, Anaximenes' ideas about air seem regressive. When, however, the idea is seen as a more general concept—as the first theory to explain a single substance capable of changing its form—its sophistication can be appreciated. Most ancient thinkers agreed that Anaximenes provided a better explanation of natural phenomena.

It is a small step from Anaximenes' ideas of rarefaction and condensation to Empedocles' definition of matter and the atomic theories of Heraclitus of Ephesus and Democritus. Clearly, no one in the modern world would take these ideas at face value, but with a small shift in the translation of Anaximeneian terms, one approaches the modern concepts of states of matter and the relationship between energy and matter. Thus, Anaximenes is an important figure in the development of Western philosophical and scientific thought.

Bibliography

Barnes, Jonathan. *The Presocratic Philosophers*. London: Routledge and Kegan Paul, 1979, rev. ed. 1982. Contains a section on Anaximenes as well as scattered comments on his ideas. Barnes is most at home with philosophical discourse and relates ancient philosophical concepts to more modern thinkers. With bibliography and concordances of ancient sources.

Burnet, John. *Early Greek Philosophy*. 4th ed. London: Adam and Charles

Black, 1930. The major ancient texts are translated and the ideas of Anaximenes discussed in this excellent work.

Guthrie, W. K. C. *A History of Greek Philosophy*. Vol. 1, *The Earlier Presocratics and the Pythagoreans*. Cambridge: Cambridge University Press, 1962. Contains an extended section on Anaximenes which is judicial and well-balanced. Guthrie's account is used as the standard by historians. With good bibliographies and concordances of ancient sources.

Hurwit, Jeffrey M. *The Art and Culture of Early Greece, 1100-480 B.C.* Ithaca, N.Y.: Cornell University Press, 1985. An exciting analysis of Greek life that integrates studies of literature, philosophy, and art.

Kirk, G. S., and J. E. Raven. *The Presocratic Philosophers*. Cambridge: Cambridge University Press, 1957. The most extensive attempt to reconstruct Anaximenes by examining all of the relevant ancient references with detailed discussions of each text. The relevant Greek and Latin texts are given, with translations provided in the notes. Includes interpretation based on the texts but little or no reference to other modern scholarly ideas. Contains concordances of ancient texts.

Stokes, M. C. *The One and Many in Presocratic Philosophy*. Washington, D.C.: Center for Hellenic Studies with Oxford University Press, 1972. While this book is not about Anaximenes, he looms large in the investigation, and Stokes's ideas about him are important. Stokes investigates the relationship between Anaximander's and Anaximenes' ideas, as well as the relationship of Anaximenes to ancient Near Eastern thought and Hesiod.

Sweeney, Leo. *Infinity in the Presocratics: A Bibliographical and Philosophical Study*. The Hague: Martinus Nijhoff, 1972. Each of the pre-Socratics is discussed in terms of his contribution to this specific topic. Important discussions on the usability of each ancient source for Anaximenes are included.

Michael M. Eisman

APOLLONIUS OF PERGA

Born: c. 240 B.C.; Perga, Asia Minor
Died: c. 170 B.C.; Alexandria, Egypt
Areas of Achievement: Mathematics and astronomy
Contribution: One of the ablest geometers in antiquity, Apollonius systematized the theory of conic sections in a treatise that remained the definitive introduction to this field until modern times. His study of circular motion established the foundation for Greek geometric astronomy.

Early Life

Information on Apollonius' life is meager. Born at Perga after the middle of the third century B.C., he studied mathematics with the successors of Euclid at Alexandria. His activity falls near the time of Archimedes (287-212 B.C.), but links between their work are indirect. In his surviving work, Apollonius once mentions the Alexandria-based geometer Conon of Samos, but his principal correspondents and colleagues (Eudemus, Philonides, Dionysodorus, Attalus I) were active at Pergamum and other centers in Asia Minor. It appears that this circle benefited from the cultural ambitions of the new Attalid dynasty during the late third and the second centuries B.C.

Life's Work

Apollonius' main achievement lies in his study of the conic sections. Two properties of these curves can be distinguished as basic for their conception: First, they are specified as the locus of points whose distances x, y from given lines satisfy certain second-order relations: When $x^2 = ay$ (for a constant line segment a) the curve of the locus is a parabola, when $x^2 = ay - ay^2/b$ the curve is an ellipse (it becomes a circle when $b = a$), and when $x^2 = ay + ay^2/b$ it is a hyperbola. The same curves can be produced when a plane intersects the surface of a cone: When the plane is parallel to the side of the cone, there results a parabola (a single open, or infinitely extending, curve); when the plane is not parallel to the side of the cone, but cuts through only one of its two sheets, there results an ellipse (a single closed curve); and when it cuts through both sheets of the cone, there results a hyperbola (a curve consisting of two separate branches, each extending indefinitely).

The curves were already known in the fourth century B.C., for the geometer Menaechmus introduced the locus forms of two parabolas and a hyperbola in order to solve the problem of doubling the cube. By the time of Euclid (c. 300 B.C.), the formation of the curves as solid sections was well understood. Euclid himself produced a major treatise on the conics, as had a geometer named Aristaeus somewhat earlier. Since Archimedes often assumes theorems on conics, one supposes that his basic reference source (which he sometimes cites as the "Conic Elements") was the Euclidean or

APOLLONII PERGÆI

CONICORUM

LIBRI OCTO,

ET

SERENI ANTISSENSIS

DE SECTIONE

CYLINDRI & CONI

LIBRI DUO.

OXONIÆ,

E THEATRO SHELDONIANO, An. Dom. MDCCX.

Aristaean textbook. Also in the third century, Eratosthenes of Cyrene and Conon pursued studies in the conics (these works no longer survive), as did Diocles in his writing on burning mirrors (extant in an Arabic translation).

Apollonius thus drew from more than a century of research on conics. In the eight books of his treatise, *Cōnica* (*Treatise on Conic Sections*, 1896; best known as *Conics*), he systematized the elements of this field and contributed many new findings of his own. Only the first four books survive in Greek, in the edition prepared by Eutocius of Ascalon (active at Alexandria in the early sixth century A.D.), but all of its books except for the eighth exist in an Arabic translation from the ninth century.

Among the topics that Apollonius covers are these: book I, the principal constructions and properties of the three types of conics, their tangents, conjugate diameters, and transformation of axes; book II, properties of hyperbolas, such as their relation to their asymptotes (the straight lines they indefinitely approach, but never meet); book III, properties of intersecting chords and secants drawn to conics; book IV, how conics intersect one another; book V, on the drawing of normal lines to conics (lines defined as the minimal distance between a curve and given points); book VI, on similar conics; book VII, properties of the conjugate diameters and principal axes of conics; book VIII (lost), problems solved via the theorems of book VII.

As Apollonius states in the prefaces to the books of his treatise, the chief application of conics is to geometric problems—that is, propositions seeking the construction of a figure satisfying specified conditions. Apollonius includes only a few examples in the *Conics*: for example, to find a cone whose section produces a conic curve of specified parameters (I 52-56), or to draw tangents and normals to given conics (II 49-53 and V 55-63). Much of the content of the *Conics*, however, deals not with problems but with theorems auxiliary to problems. This is the case with book III, for example, which Apollonius says is especially useful for problem solving, but which actually contains no problems. In his preface, he explicitly mentions the problem of the "locus relative to three (or four) lines," all cases of which, Apollonius proudly asserts, can be worked out by means of his book III, whereas Euclid's earlier effort was incomplete.

The significance of problem solving for the Greek geometric tradition is evident in works such as Euclid's *Stoicheia* (*Elements*) and *Ta dedomena* (*Data*). In more advanced fields such as conic theory, however, the surviving evidence is only barely representative of the richness of this ancient activity. A notable exception is the *Synagogē* (*Collection*), a massive anthology of geometry by Pappus of Alexandria (fourth century A.D.), which preserves many examples of problems. Indeed, the whole of its book VII amounts to an extended commentary on the problem solving tradition—what Pappus calls the "analytic corpus" (*topos analyomenos*), a group of twelve treatises by Euclid, Apollonius, and others. Of the works taken from Apollonius, two are extant—*Conics* and *Logou apotomē* (*On Cutting Off a Ratio*, 1987)—while another five are lost—*Chōriou apotomē* (cutting off an area), *Diōrismenē tomē* (determinate section), *Epaphai* (tangencies), *Neyseis* (vergings), and *Topoi epipedoi* (plane loci). Pappus' summaries and technical notes preserve the best evidence available regarding the content of these lost works. Thus it is known that in *Epaphai*, for example, Apollonius covered all possible ways of constructing a circle so as to touch any combination of three given elements (points, lines, or circles); in *Neyseis* he sought the position of a line verging toward a given point and such that a marked segment of it lies exactly between given lines or circles; in *Topoi epipedoi* circles were produced as loci satisfying stated conditions, several of these being equivalent to expressions now familiar in analytic geometry.

It is significant that these last three works were restricted to planar constructions—that is, ones requiring only circles and straight lines. Pappus classifies problems in three categories: In addition to the planar, he names the solid (solvable by conics) and the linear (solvable by special curves, such as certain curves of third order, or others, such as spirals, now termed "transcendental," composed of coordinated circular and rectilinear motions). For Pappus, this scheme is normative; a planar solution, if known, is preferable to a solid one, and, similarly, a solid solution to a linear. For example, the problems of circle quadrature, cube duplication, and angle trisection can be solved by linear curves, but the last two can also be solved by conics and so are classed as solid. Historians often misinterpret this classification as a restriction on solutions, as if the ancients accepted only the planar constructions. To the contrary, geometers throughout antiquity so fully explored all forms of construction as to belie any such restriction. Presumably, in his three books on planar constructions, Apollonius sought to specify as completely as possible the domain of such constructions rather than to eliminate those of the solid or linear type. In any event, from works before Apollonius there is no evidence at all of a normative conception of problem-solving methods.

There survive isolated reports of Apollonian studies bearing on the regular solids, the cylindrical spiral, irrationals, circle measurement, the arithmetic of large numbers, and other topics. For the most part, little is known of these efforts, and their significance was slight in comparison with his treatises on geometric constructions.

Ptolemy reports in *Mathēmatikē suntaxis* (c. A.D. 150; *Almagest*) that Apollonius made a significant contribution to astronomical theory by establishing the geometric condition for a planet to appear stationary relative to the fixed stars. Since, according to Ptolemy, he proved this condition for both the epicyclic and the eccentric models of planetary motion, Apollonius seems to have had some major responsibility for the introduction of these basic models. Apollonius studied only the geometric properties of these models, however, for the project of adapting them to actual planetary data became a concern only for astronomers such as Hipparchus a few decades later in the second century B.C.

Summary

If Apollonius of Perga did indeed institute the eccentric and epicyclic models for planetary motion, as seems likely, he merits the appellation assigned to him by historian Otto Neugebauer: "the founder of Greek mathematical astronomy." These geometric devices, when adjusted to observational data and made suitable for numerical computation, became the basis of the sophisticated Greek system of astronomy. Through its codification by Ptolemy in the *Almagest*, this system flourished among Arabic and Hindu astronomers in the Middle Ages and Latin astronomers in the West through the sixteenth century. Although Nicolaus Copernicus (1473-1543) made the significant change of replacing Ptolemy's geocentric arrangement with a heliocentric one, even he retained the basic geometric methods of the older system. Only with Johannes Kepler (1571-1630), who was first to substitute elliptical orbits for the configurations of circles in the Ptolemaic-Copernican scheme, can one speak of a clear break with the mathematical methods of ancient astronomy.

Apollonius' work in geometry fared quite differently. The fields of conics and advanced geometric constructions he so fully explored came to a virtual dead end soon after his time. The complexity of this subject, proliferating in special cases and lacking convenient notations (such as the algebraic forms, for example, of modern analytic geometry that first appeared only with François Viète, René Descartes, and Pierre de Fermat in the late sixteenth and the seventeenth centuries), must have discouraged further research among geometers in the second century B.C.

In later antiquity, interest in Apollonius' work revived: Pappus and Hypatia of Alexandria (fourth to early fifth century A.D.) and Eutocius (sixth century) produced commentaries on the *Conics*. Their work did not extend the field in any significant way beyond what Apollonius had done, but it proved critical for the later history of conic theory, by ensuring the survival of Apollonius' writing. When the *Conics* was translated into Arabic in the ninth century, Arabic geometers entered this field; they approached the study of Apollonius with considerable inventiveness, often devising new forms of proofs, or contributing new results where the texts at their disposal were incomplete. Alhazen (early eleventh century), for example, attempted a restoration of Apollonius' lost book VIII.

In the early modern period, after the publication of the translations of Apollonius and Pappus by Federigo Commandino in 1588-1589, the study of advanced geometry received new impetus in the West. Several distinguished mathematicians in this period (François Viète, Willebrord Snel, Pierre de Fermat, Edmond Halley, and others) tried their hand at restoring lost analytic works of Apollonius. The entirely new field of projective geometry emerged from the conic researches of Gérard Desargues and Blaise Pascal in the seventeenth century. Thus, the creation of the modern field of geometry owes much to the stimulus of the *Conics* and the associated treatises of Apollonius.

Bibliography

Apollonius. *On Cutting Off a Ratio*. Translated by Edward Macierowski. Fairfield, Conn.: Golden Hind Press, 1987. This translation is literal and provisional; a full critical edition is being prepared by Macierowski.

———. *Treatise on Conic Sections*. Translated and edited by Thomas Little Heath. Cambridge: Cambridge University Press, 1896. Translation in modern notation, with extensive commentary. Heath surveys the older history of conics, including efforts by Euclid and Archimedes, and then summarizes the characteristic terminology and methods used by Apollonius. A synopsis appears in Heath's *History of Greek Mathematics* (Oxford: Clarendon Press, 1921), together with ample discussions of the lost Apollonian treatises described by Pappus.

Hogemdijk, J. P. *Ibn al-Haytham's Completion of the "Conics."* New York: Springer-Verlag, 1984. This edition of the Arabic text of Alhazen's restoration of the lost book VIII of the *Conics* is accompanied by a literal English translation, a mathematical summary in modern notation, and discussions of the Greek and Arabic traditions of Apollonius' work. See also Hogemdijk's "Arabic Traces of Lost Works of Apollonius" in *Archive for History of Exact Sciences* 35 (1986): 187-253, which represents an edition, with English translation, of medieval Arabic documents revealing knowledge of certain works of Apollonius.

Knorr, W. R. *Ancient Tradition of Geometric Problems*. Cambridge, Mass.: Birkhauser Boston, 1986. A survey of Greek geometric methods from the pre-Euclidean period to late antiquity. Chapter 7 is devoted to the work of Apollonius, including his *Conics* and lost analytic writings.

Neugebauer, Otto. *A History of Ancient Mathematical Astronomy*. New York: Springer-Verlag, 1975. The section on Apollonius in this work provides a detailed technical account of his contributions to ancient astronomy.

Pappus of Alexandria. *Book 7 of the "Collection."* Translated by A. Jones. New York: Springer-Verlag, 1986. A critical edition of Pappus' Greek text (collated with the former edition of F. Hultsch in volume 2 of *Pappi Collectionis Quae Supersunt*, 1877), with English translation and commentary. Pappus' book preserves highly valuable information on Apollonius' lost works on geometric construction. Jones surveys in detail Pappus' evidence of the lost works and modern efforts to reconstruct them.

Toomer, G. J. "Apollonius of Perga." In *Dictionary of Scientific Biography*, vol. 1. New York: Charles Scribner's Sons, 1970. What is known of Apollonius' life and work is here summarized, with an extensive bibliography. For a discussion of the earlier field of conics, see also Toomer's translation of Diocles' *Peri pyreiōn*: *Diocles on Burning Mirrors* (New York: Springer-Verlag, 1976).

Waerden, Bartel Leendert van der. *Science Awakening*. Translated by Arnold Dresden. Groningen, Netherlands: Noordhoff, 1954. In this highly readable survey of ancient mathematics, Waerden includes a useful synopsis of the geometric work of Apollonius.

Zeuthen, H. G. *Die Lehre von den Kegelschnitten im Altertum*. Copenhagen: Höst and Sohn, 1886. The definitive modern study of Apollonius' work in the conics, with detailed discussions also of the earlier history of the conics and of Apollonius' lost works. Zeuthen's principal theses are discussed by Heath, Toomer, Jones, and Knorr (see above).

Wilbur R. Knorr

ARCHIMEDES

Born: 287 B.C.; Syracuse, Sicily
Died: 212 B.C.; Syracuse, Sicily
Areas of Achievement: Science, mathematics, and engineering
Contribution: The greatest mathematician of antiquity, Archimedes did his best work in geometry and also founded the disciplines of statics and hydrostatics.

Early Life

Few details are certain about the life of Archimedes. His birth in 287 B.C. was established from a report, about fourteen hundred years after the fact, that he was seventy-five years old at his death in 212 B.C. Ancient writers agree in calling him a Syracusan by birth, and he himself provides the information that his father was the astronomer Pheidias, the author of a treatise on the diameters of the sun and moon. His father's profession suggests an explanation for the son's early interest in astronomy and mathematics. Some scholars have characterized Archimedes as an aristocrat who actively participated in the Syracusan court and who may have been related to King Hieron II, the ruler of Syracuse. He certainly was friendly with Hieron and Hieron's son Gelon, to whom he dedicated one of his works. (Original titles of Archimedes' works are not known, but most of his books were first translated into English in 1897 in the volume *Works*.)

Archimedes traveled to Egypt to study in Alexandria, then the center of the scientific world. Some of his teachers had, in their youth, been students of Euclid. He made two close friends in Alexandria: Conon of Samos, a gifted mathematician, and Eratosthenes of Cyrene, also a good mathematician. From the prefaces to his works, it is clear that Archimedes maintained friendly relations with several Alexandrian scholars, and he played an active role in developing the mathematical traditions of this intellectual center. It is possible that he visited Spain before returning to Syracuse, and a return trip to Egypt is also a possibility. This second visit would have been the occasion for his construction of dikes and bridges reported in some Arabian sources.

In Syracuse, Archimedes spent his time working on mathematical and mechanical problems. Although he was a remarkably ingenious inventor, his inventions were, according to Plutarch, merely diversions, the work of a geometer at play. He possessed such a lofty intellect that he considered these inventions of much less worth than his mathematical creations. Plutarch may have exaggerated Archimedes' distaste for engineering, because there is evidence that he was fascinated by mechanical problems from a practical as well as theoretical point of view.

In the stories that multiplied about him, Archimedes became a symbol of the learned man—absentminded and unconcerned with food, clothing, and

Library of Congress

the other necessities of life. In images created long after his death, he is depicted as the quintessential sage, with a heavily bearded face, massive forehead, and contemplative mien. He had a good sense of humor. For example, he often sent his theorems to Alexandria, but to play a trick on some conceited mathematicians there, he once slipped in a few false propositions, so that these individuals, who pretended to have discovered everything by themselves, would fall into the trap of proposing theorems that were impossible.

Life's Work

The range of Archimedes' interest was wide, encompassing statics, hydrostatics, optics, astronomy, and engineering, in addition to geometry and arithmetic. It is natural that stories should tell more about his engineering inventiveness than his mathematical ability, for clever machines appealed to the average mind more than abstract mathematical theorems. Unfortunately, many of these stories are doubtful. For example, Archimedes is supposed to have invented a hollow, helical cylinder that, when rotated, could serve as a water pump, but this device, now called the Archimedean screw, antedates its supposed inventor.

In another well-known story, Archimedes boasted to King Hieron that, if he had a place on which to stand, he could move the earth. Hieron urged him to make good this boast by hauling ashore a fully loaded three-masted merchantman of the royal fleet. Using a compound pulley, Archimedes, with modest effort, pulled the ship out of the harbor and onto the shore. The compound pulley may have been Archimedes' invention, but the story, told by Plutarch, is probably a legend.

The most famous story about Archimedes is attributed to Vitruvius, a Roman architect under Emperor Augustus. King Hieron, grateful for the success of one of his ventures, wanted to thank the gods by consecrating a golden wreath. Upon delivery, the wreath had the weight of the gold supplied for it, but Hieron suspected that it had been adulterated with silver. Unable to make the goldsmith confess, Hieron asked Archimedes to devise some way of testing the wreath. Since it was a consecrated object, Archimedes could not subject it to chemical analysis. He pondered the problem without success until one day, when he entered a full bath, he noticed that the deeper he descended into the tub, the more water flowed over the edge. This suggested to him that the amount of overflowed water was equal in volume to the portion of his body submerged in the bath. This observation gave him a way of solving the problem, and he was so overjoyed that he leapt out of the tub and ran home naked through the streets, shouting: "Eureka! Eureka!" Vitruvius then goes on to explain how Archimedes made use of his newly gained insight. By putting the wreath into water, he could tell by the rise in water level the volume of the wreath. He also dipped into water lumps of gold and silver, each having the same weight as the wreath. He found that the wreath caused more water to overflow than the gold and less than the silver. From this experiment, he determined the amount of silver admixed with the gold in the wreath.

As amusing and instructive as these legends are, much more reliable and interesting to modern historians of science are Archimedes' mathematical works. These treatises can be divided into three groups: studies of figures bounded by curved lines and surfaces, works on the geometrical analysis of statical and hydrostatical problems, and arithmetical works. The form in which these treatises have survived is not the form in which they left Archimedes' hand: They have all undergone transformations and emendations. Nevertheless, one still finds the spirit of Archimedes in the intricacy of the questions and the lucidity of the explanations.

In finding the areas of plane figures bounded by curved lines and the volumes of solid figures bounded by curved surfaces, Archimedes used a method originated by Eudoxus of Cnidus, unhappily called the "method of exhaustion." This indirect proof involves inscribing and circumscribing polygons to approach a length, area, or volume. The name "exhaustion" is based on the idea that, for example, a circle would finally be exhausted by inscribed polygons with a growing number of sides. In *On the Sphere and Cylinder*, Archimedes compares perimeters of inscribed and circumscribed polygons to prove that the volume of a sphere is two-thirds the volume of its circumscribed cylinder. He also proves that the surface of any sphere is four times the area of its greatest circle.

Having successfully applied this method to the sphere and cylinder, Archimedes went on to use the technique for many other figures, including spheroids, spirals, and parabolas. *On Conoids and Spheroids* treats the figures of revolution generated by conics. His spheroids are what are now called oblate and prolate spheroids, which are figures of revolution generated by ellipses. Archimedes' object in this work was the determination of volumes of segments cut off by planes from these conoidal and spheroidal solids. In *On Spirals*, Archimedes studies the area enclosed between successive whorls of a spiral. He also defines a figure, now called Archimedes' spiral: If a ray from a central point rotates uniformly about this point, like the hand of a clock, and if another point moves uniformly along this line (marked by the clock hand), starting at the central point, then this linearly moving and rotating point will trace Archimedes' spiral.

Quadrature of the Parabola is not Archimedes' original title for the treatise, since "parabola" was not used in the sense of a conic section in the third century B.C. On the other hand, quadrature is an ancient term: It denotes the process of constructing a square equal in area to a given surface, in this case a parabolic segment. Archimedes, in this treatise, proves the theorem that the area of a parabolic segment is four-thirds the area of its greatest inscribed triangle. He is so fond of this theorem that he gives different proofs for it. One proof uses a method of exhaustion in which the parabolic segment is "exhausted" by a series of triangles. The other consists of establishing the quadrature of the parabola by mechanically balancing elements of the unknown area against elements of a known area. This latter method gives an insight into how Archimedes discovered theorems to be proved. His most recently discovered work, *Method of Mechanical Theorems* (translated in 1912), provides other examples of how Archimedes mathematically balanced geometrical figures as if they were on a weighing balance. He did not consider that this mechanical method constituted a demonstration, but it allowed him to find interesting theorems, which he then proved by more rigorous geometrical methods.

Archimedes also applied geometry to statics and hydrostatics successfully. In his *The Equilibrium of Planes*, he proves the law of the lever geometrically and then puts it to use in finding the centers of gravity of several thin sheets of different shapes. By center of gravity, Archimedes meant the point at which the object can be supported so as to be in equilibrium under the pull of gravity. Earlier Greek mathematicians had made use of the principle of the lever in showing that a small weight at a large distance from a fulcrum would balance a large weight near the fulcrum, but Archimedes worked this principle out in mathematical detail. In his proof, the weights become geometrical magnitudes acting perpendicularly to the balance beam, which itself is conceived as a weightless geometrical line. In this way, he reduced statics to a rigorous discipline comparable to what Euclid had done for geometry.

Archimedes once more emphasizes geometrical analysis in *On Floating Bodies*. The cool logic of this treatise contrasts with his emotional discovery of the buoyancy principle. In this work, he proves that solids lighter than a fluid will, when placed in the fluid, sink to the depth where the weight of the solid will be equal to the weight of the fluid displaced. Solids heavier than the fluid will, when placed in the fluid, sink to the bottom, and they will be lighter by the weight of the displaced fluid.

Although Archimedes' investigations were primarily in geometry and mechanics, he did perform some interesting studies in numerical calculation. For example, in *Measurement of the Circle* he calculated, based on mathematical principles rather than direct measurement, a value for the ratio of the circumference of a circle to its diameter (this ratio was not called pi until much later). By inscribing and circumscribing regular polygons of more and more sides within and around a circle, Archimedes found that the ratio was between $223/71$ and $220/70$, the best value for π (pi) ever obtained in the classical world.

In *The Sand-Reckoner*, Archimedes devises a notation suitable for writing very large numbers. To put this new notation to a test, he sets down a number equal to the number of grains of sand it would take to fill the entire universe. Large numbers are also involved in his treatise concerned with the famous “Cattle Problem.” White, black, yellow, and dappled cows and bulls are grazing on the island of Sicily. The numbers of these cows and bulls have to satisfy several conditions. The problem is to find the number of bulls and cows of each of the four colors. It is unlikely that Archimedes ever completely solved this problem in indeterminate analysis.

Toward the end of his life, Archimedes became part of a worsening political situation. His friend Hieron II had a treaty of alliance with Rome and remained faithful to it, even after the Second Punic War began. After his death, however, his grandson Hieronymus, who became king, was so impressed by Hannibal’s victories in Italy that he switched sides to Carthage. Hieronymus was then assassinated, but Sicily remained allied with Carthage. Consequently, the Romans sent a fleet under the command of Marcellus to capture Syracuse. According to traditional stories, Archimedes invented devices for warding off the Roman enemy. He is supposed to have constructed large lenses to set the fleet on fire and mechanical cranes to turn ships upside down. He devised so many ingenious war machines that the Romans would flee if so much as a piece of rope appeared above a wall. These stories are grossly exaggerated if not totally fabricated, but Archimedes may have helped in the defense of his city, and he certainly provided the Romans with a face-saving explanation for their frustratingly long siege of Syracuse.

Because of treachery by a cabal of nobles, among other things, Syracuse eventually fell. Marcellus ordered that the city be sacked, but he made it clear that his soldiers were to spare the house and person of Archimedes. Amid the confusion of the sack, however, Archimedes, while puzzling over a geometrical diagram drawn on sand in a tray, was killed by a Roman soldier. During his lifetime he had expressed the wish that upon his tomb should be placed a cylinder circumscribing a sphere, together with an inscription giving the ratio between the volumes of these two bodies, a discovery of which he was especially proud. Marcellus, who was distressed by the great mathematician’s death, had Archimedes’ wish carried out. More than a century later, when Cicero was in Sicily, he found this tomb, overgrown with brush but with the figure of the sphere and cylinder still visible.

Summary

Some scholars rank Archimedes with Sir Isaac Newton and Carl Friedrich Gauss as one of the three greatest mathematicians who ever lived, and historians of mathematics agree that the theorems Archimedes discovered raised Greek mathematics to a new level of understanding. He tackled very difficult and original problems and solved them through boldness and vision. His skill in using mechanical ideas in mathematics was paralleled by his ingenious use of mathematics in mechanics.

The Latin West received its knowledge of Archimedes from two sources:

Byzantium and Islam. His works were translated from the Greek and Arabic into Latin in the twelfth century and played an important role in stimulating the work of medieval natural philosophers. Knowledge of Archimedes' ideas multiplied during the Renaissance, and by the seventeenth century his insights had been almost completely absorbed into European thought and had deeply influenced the birth of modern science. For example, Galileo was inspired by Archimedes and tried to do for dynamics what Archimedes had done for statics. More than any other ancient scientist, Archimedes observed the world in a way that modern scientists from Galileo to Albert Einstein admired and sought to emulate.

Bibliography

Aaboe, Asger. *Episodes from the Early History of Mathematics*. New York: Random House, 1964. After a brief account of Archimedes' life and a survey of his works, the third chapter of this book presents three samples of Archimedean mathematics: the trisection of an angle, the construction of a regular heptagon, and the determination of a sphere's volume and surface area.

Bell, E. T. *Men of Mathematics*. New York: Simon and Schuster, 1937. A widely available popular collection of biographical essays on the world's greatest mathematicians. Bell discusses Archimedes, along with Zeno of Elea and Eudoxus, in an early chapter on "Modern Minds in Ancient Bodies."

Clagett, Marshall. "Archimedes." In *Dictionary of Scientific Biography*, edited by Charles Couston Gillispie, vol. 1. New York: Charles Scribner's Sons, 1970. Clagett is an eminent scholar of Archimedes, and in his five-volume work, *Archimedes in the Middle Ages* (1964-1984), he has traced the medieval Latin tradition of Archimedes' works. This article makes his major insights on Archimedes available to the general reader.

Dijksterhuis, E. J. *Archimedes*. Princeton, N.J.: Princeton University Press, 1987. This edition of the best survey in English of Archimedes' life and work also contains a valuable bibliographical essay by Wilbur R. Knorr.

Finley, Moses I. *A History of Sicily*. Vol. 1, *Ancient Sicily*. New York: Viking Press, 1968. Finley's account of the history of Sicily from antiquity to the Arab conquest has a section explaining how the politics of the Second Punic War led to Archimedes' death.

Heath, T. L. *A History of Greek Mathematics*. 2 vols. Oxford: Clarendon Press, 1921. A good general survey of ancient Greek mathematics that contains, in volume 2, a detailed account of the works of Archimedes. This book and the author's *Works of Archimedes* (1897, with supplement 1912) unfortunately use modern notation, which risks misrepresenting the thrust of Archimedes' proofs.

Kline, Morris. *Mathematical Thought from Ancient to Modern Times*. New

York: Oxford University Press, 1972. Kline's aim is to present the chief ideas that have shaped the history of mathematics rather than the people involved. Consequently, his treatment of Archimedes emphasizes the themes of his work rather than the events of his life.

Lloyd, G. E. R. *Greek Science After Aristotle*. New York: W. W. Norton and Co., 1973. Lloyd's book, intended for the general reader, centers on the interaction of Hellenistic science and mathematics with religion, philosophy, and technology. It contains a brief but good account of the life and work of Archimedes in this larger intellectual context.

Van der Waerden, B. L. *Science Awakening*. New York: John Wiley and Sons, 1963. A survey of ancient Egyptian, Babylonian, and Greek mathematics. The chapter on the Alexandrian era (330-220 B.C.) contains a detailed account of Archimedes' life, legends, and mathematical accomplishments.

Robert J. Paradowski

ARETAEUS OF CAPPADOCIA

Born: Probably second century A.D.; Cappadocia, Roman Empire
Died: Date unknown; place unknown
Area of Achievement: Medicine
Contribution: Considered by many the greatest ancient physician after Hippocrates, Aretaeus wrote the best and most accurate descriptions of many diseases and made landmark studies of diabetes and neurological and mental disorders.

Early Life

Not even the exact century of Aretaeus of Cappadocia's birth is known; most scholars agree on the second century A.D., although a few offer the first or third century. Aretaeus' epithet is "Cappadocian," implying that he was born in that most eastern of Roman provinces. No other information about his life is certain. Scholars conjecture, however, that he studied in Egypt at Alexandria, founded in 331 B.C. as the major center for medical study, research, and teaching. Aretaeus mentions Egypt in his works and describes its geography and some diseases and therapeutics unique to that country. Some scholars also believe that Aretaeus practiced medicine in Rome; he prescribed wines known to second century Rome—namely, Falernian, Fundian, Sequine, and Surrentine.

Aretaeus was an Eclectic by practice and a Pneumatist by training. After Hippocrates in the fifth century B.C. there was little advance in the knowledge of disease and its treatment, although there were significant gains at Alexandria in the area of anatomy because of the dissections of human bodies. Instead, post-Hippocratic physicians tended to theorize about medicine as a philosophy and to develop various schools of medicine. Dogmatism and Empiricism were the first schools. The Dogmatists employed theoretical principles; they believed that reason and systematic studies of anatomy and physiology were necessary for the physician. The Empiricists, on the other hand, rejected theory and anatomy; they stressed experience and observation. The "tripod" of the Empiricists' knowledge was personal observation, researched historical observation, and use of analogy in analyzing unknown cases.

Two schools developed in reaction to the Dogmatists and Empiricists. Methodism, founded in the late first century B.C., rejected the theory of the humors so prevalent in Hippocratic medicine and advocated an atomic stance. The Methodists considered disease an interference of the normal position and motion of the atoms in the human body; treatments were prescribed to restore the proper order of the atoms—relaxants to counteract excessive tension, astringents to counteract excessive looseness.

The Pneumatic school, established around A.D. 50 by Athenaeus of Atta-

Library of Congress

leia, stressed *pneuma*, meaning "vital air" or "breath." The beliefs of the Pneumatists were a combination of the Stoic philosophy, with its emphasis on primordial matter, the *pneuma*, from which all life comes, and Hippocratic pathology. Disease occurs when an imbalance of the four humors (blood, phlegm, black bile, and yellow bile) disturbs the *pneuma* in the human body.

Each of these various schools had both strengths and glaring weaknesses in their theories and practices. The knowledge of these weaknesses, coupled with Roman common sense, which rejected the Greek love of theory, led most Roman physicians, beginning with Archigenes (who flourished around A.D. 100), to pick and choose among the various doctrines and ideas of the four schools. Such physicians were called Eclectics. That Aretaeus was an Eclectic is obvious from his work: For example, although he followed Pneumatism in its concept of the vital breath and its relation to the four humors, Aretaeus pursued anatomy and physiology avidly, as the Dogmatists did, yet he also relied heavily on observation and experience in the manner of an Empiricist; his emphasis on simple regimens and treatments recalls the Methodist school as well as Hippocrates.

Life's Work

Aretaeus refused to be dogmatic and speculative. He attempted to describe diseases in clear, scientific, and rational terms, and his writings bear the marks of careful thought and extensive clinical experience. Aretaeus wrote seven works, two of which survive: *Peri aition kai semeion oxeon kai chronion pathon* (*On the Causes and Symptoms of Acute and Chronic Diseases*, 1856) and *Oxeon kai chronion nouson therapeutikon biblion* (*Book on the Treatment of Acute and Chronic Diseases*, 1856). The lost works discussed fevers, surgery, pharmacology, gynecology, and prophylaxis. Aretaeus wrote in Ionic Greek, a dialect which had not been in use for centuries; he chose the Ionic style to imitate Hippocrates, who also wrote in that dialect.

Aretaeus followed the Methodist classification of diseases into chronic and acute; the distinction was made on the course of the disease, that is, whether the disease lasted over a long period of time or was of a short duration and reached a "crisis" (the point in the progress of the disease when the patient recovered or died). Chronic diseases include paralysis, migraine headaches, and insanity, while examples of acute diseases are pneumonia, pleurisy, tetanus, and diphtheria. Aretaeus' descriptions of these and other diseases show him to be an accurate observer who was concerned more for the patient than for theory itself. His accounts, so important in the history of medicine, may be summarized in the following categories: anatomy and physiology, symptomatology (physical description of diseases such as diabetes, leprosy, and ulcers), neurology and psychiatry, surgery, and therapeutics.

Aretaeus devoted more attention to anatomy and physiology than most ancient physicians. As stated earlier, Aretaeus followed the Pneumatist doctrine: He believed that the body is composed of the four humors and of spirit (*pneuma*), and the proper mixture and interplay of these elements constitutes health. Blood is formed in the liver from food; phlegm is secreted by the brain into the other organs; yellow bile comes from the liver, black bile from the spleen. The most important organ is the heart, since the heart is the site of heat and *pneuma*. The heart draws the *pneuma* from the lungs, which are stimulated by it. Respiration itself depends upon the movement of the thorax and diaphragm and also upon the lungs' contraction and expansion. Regarding the nervous system, nerves originate in the brain; this idea was based on the perception that the spinal cord was a prolongation of the brain. All nerves cross between their origin in the brain and their final termination in the body; Aretaeus based this belief on his startling observation that a cerebral lesion caused paralysis on the opposite side of the body.

Aretaeus knew much about circulation. The aorta, he stated, comes from the heart and is located to the left of the vena cava; the aorta carries the *pneuma* to the other organs. The veins, which originate in the liver, bring the blood to all the body. Aretaeus asserted that the content of the arteries was light-colored, that of the veins dark. The liver itself is composed mostly of blood and produces blood and bile; if it becomes inflamed, jaundice results. Aretaeus wrote remarkable accounts of the kidneys and the bile ducts. He thought of the kidneys as cavities which acted like sieves for collecting urine and were connected to the bladder by two tubes, one from each kidney. Digestion of food occurs not only in the stomach but also in the intestines. The portal vein takes the food after digestion to the liver, where it is taken out as blood by the vena cava to the heart. This scheme shows that Aretaeus was aware of nearly all circulatory processes and the direction of blood flow in the veins.

One of Aretaeus' greatest accomplishments was his practice of physical diagnosis. He used anatomical inspection, distinguishing the appearances of ulcers in the small and large bowels, for example. Also, before he discussed a disease, Aretaeus prefixed an anatomical and physiological introduction concerning the part(s) of the body afflicted by the disease (this is the method used in many modern medical textbooks). In his physical examinations, Aretaeus employed auscultation of the heart, palpitation of the body (to check for enlargement of the liver and spleen), and percussion of the abdomen. Aretaeus always noted carefully the patient's symptoms: temperature, breathing, pulse, secretions, color of skin, and condition of the pupils. In the tradition of Hippocrates, Aretaeus related diseases to foods eaten by the patient and to climate, time of year, and environment.

Aretaeus' symptomatology is considered excellent by medical historians and, in some instances, not improved upon even by contemporary medicine. Especially praiseworthy are Aretaeus' accounts of hematemesis, jaundice, dropsy, tuberculosis, tetanus, epilepsy, and cardiac syncope. Aretaeus distinguished between pneumonia and pleurisy and is credited with the initial descriptions of diphtheria and asthma. He was the first European to write a symptomatic account of diabetes, and he gave the disease its name. Aretaeus correctly thought of diabetes as a progressive form of dropsy with polyuria and excessive thirst that results in emaciation of flesh. Finally, Aretaeus' accounts of leprosy are invaluable. He offered useful distinctions between the types of leprosy: elephantiasis (the tuberous form of leprosy) and the maculo-anesthetic form, which involves mutilation of the body; he also provided the first recorded instance of isolating lepers and distinguished between conveyance of disease by actual contact (contagion) and transmission of disease at a distance (infection).

Aretaeus' discussions of neurological and mental diseases are important. He divided such illnesses into acute and chronic classes. The acute diseases, as he described them, are phrenitis (a febrile delirium or, at times, meningitis); lethargy (a comatose state, or encephalitis); marasmus (atrophy); apoplexy (an acute form of paralysis); tetanus; and epileptic paroxysm. Chronic diseases include cephalaea (migraine headache), vertigo (chronic paralysis), and all forms of insanity. Especially important are Aretaeus' astute distinctions between apoplexy, paraplegia, paresis, and paralysis; the basis of division was the extent of loss of movement and sensation. Aretaeus was the first to distinguish between spinal and cerebral paralysis: When the paralysis is spinal, it occurs on the same side as the lesion; when cerebral, the paralysis occurs on the opposite side (crossed paralysis).

Aretaeus' clear and full discussion of the different kinds of insanity has remained unsurpassed. He noted the stages by which intermittent insanity (manic depression) can become a senile melancholia that does not remit. While the former may be treated by phlebotomy, wormwood, and black hellebore (a plant that produces violent shocks to the nervous system similar to those in modern electric shock treatment), senile melancholia is incurable.

Aretaeus' book on surgery has been lost; he did, however, refer to surgery throughout his extant writings. Aretaeus recommended craniotomy (trepanning) for epilepsy and for cephalalgia and cephalaea (acute and chronic headache, respectively). He used catheters for urological diseases and mentioned surgery to remove kidney stones. It should be noted that surgery was not commonly practiced in antiquity, but when it was deemed necessary, the practicing physician usually performed it.

Aretaeus' treatments of disease are conservative. As in his discussions of the causes and forms of diseases, Aretaeus relied on experience and common sense, not abstract theory. He rejected tracheotomy and pleaded for extreme caution in the application of phlebotomy, venesection, cupping, and leeches: Aretaeus argued that only in severe cases should much blood be removed. Instead, he used purgatives, emetics, suppositories, laxatives, ointments, and poultices. Aretaeus also stressed exercise, massages, baths, temperate lifestyles, and a healthy diet including milk, fruits, vegetables, and foods without starch and fat. It is interesting that Aretaeus also prescribed opium for people afflicted with feverish delirium.

Summary

No ancient medical writer, except perhaps Hippocrates, surpassed Aretaeus of Cappadocia for vividness and clarity in the description of diseases. Aretaeus' descriptions of diabetes, tetanus, diphtheria, leprosy, asthma, and mental and neurological disorders are especially valuable and are landmarks in medical history. Aretaeus tried his best to put his symptomatology on a sound anatomical basis; for every disease, he supplied splendid accounts of anatomy. He gave therapeutics and cures for every disease, acute and chronic; his treatments are simple and rational. In his writings, Aretaeus was perhaps the most unbiased physician in antiquity, rejecting dogmatic thought, theory, and superstition. Finally, Aretaeus was unique in refusing to abandon the patient who was incurable; while even Hippocrates recommended turning away hopeless cases, Aretaeus ordered all measures to be taken, and, when those failed, he offered support and sympathy.

Bibliography

Allbutt, Sir Thomas. *Greek Medicine in Rome*. New York: Macmillan, 1921. Still one of the best textbooks on the medical schools and the practice of medicine in the Roman Empire. Chapter 11 ("Some Pneumatist and Eclectic Physicians") discusses Aretaeus and is superb in providing background information to the Eclectic and his writings.

Aretaeus of Cappadocia. *The Extant Works of Aretaeus the Cappadocian*. Edited and translated by Francis Adams. London: Sydenham Society, 1856. Reprint. Boston: Milford House, 1972. The only available translation of Aretaeus' work. The introduction to Aretaeus, his background, and his work is somewhat difficult for the nonspecialist, and the antiquated English of the translation is forbidding.

Cordell, E. F. "Aretaeus of Cappadocia." *Bulletin of The Johns Hopkins Hospital* 20 (1909): 371-377. This volume provides a very useful discussion of the physiology, symptomatology, and therapy in Aretaeus' works. Intended for a knowledgeable but general audience.

Leopold, Eugene. "Aretaeus the Cappadocian: His Contribution to Diabetes Mellitus." *Annals of Medical History* 2 (1930): 424-435. An excellent, straightforward account of Aretaeus' life and writings. Especially good is the discussion of Aretaeus' place in the history of medicine and diabetes. Very readable.

Mettler, Cecilia. *History of Medicine*. Philadelphia: Blakiston Co., 1947. Mettler offers an exhaustive survey of Aretaeus' discussions and treatments of diseases. One must use the index, however, as the accounts are scattered throughout the text according to typology of disease.

Neuburger, Max. *History of Medicine*. Translated by Ernest Playfair. London: Oxford Medical Publications, 1910. This classic text has useful chapters on the Pneumatists and Eclectics and Aretaeus, in particular. With invaluable discussions of the various medical schools of Aretaeus' time.

Robinson, Victor. *Pathfinders in Medicine*. New York: Medical Life Press, 1929. This volume includes an essay on Aretaeus designed for lay readers. It is excellent as a general introduction to Aretaeus, although it lacks references and notes.

Stannard, J. "Materia Medica and Philosophic Theory in Aretaeus." *Sudhoffs Archiv für Geschichte der Medizin und der Naturwissenschaften* 48 (March, 1964): 27-53. Contains extensive discussion of the therapeutics, especially dietetics, of Aretaeus. Invaluable for information on Aretaeus and his relation to Pneumatism.

Steven M. Oberhelman

ARISTOTLE

Born: 384 B.C.; Stagirus, Chalcidice, Greece
Died: 322 B.C.; Chalcis, Euboea, Greece
Areas of Achievement: Philosophy, ethics, natural history, and science
Contribution: Building on Plato's dialogical approach, Aristotle developed what is known as the scientific method. In addition, he founded the Lyceum, the second university-type institution (after Plato's Academy), which, with its vast collections of biological specimens and manuscripts of verse and prose, housed the first research library.

Early Life

Aristotle was born in the town of Stagirus, located on the northeast coast of the Chalcidice Peninsula in Greece, most likely in 384 B.C. His father, Nicomachus, was a physician and a member of the clan, or guild, of the Asclepiadae, as had been his ancestors; the family probably had migrated from Messenia in the eighth or seventh century B.C. Aristotle's mother was from Chalcis, the place where he sought refuge during the last year of his life. Both parents died while Aristotle was very young.

Aristotle was adopted and reared by Proxenus, court physician to Amyntas II of Macedonia (an occasional source suggests that Nicomachus also held this position, but others disagree); it is likely, therefore, that young Aristotle lived part of his youth at Pella, the royal seat. He may even have learned and practiced surgery during this time.

Aristotle's early environmental influences helped determine his outlook: his detached, objective way of looking at a subject, his interest in biological science, and his universality. In his early life, Aristotle was surrounded by physicians and princes, not philosophers. When he was eighteen, he was sent to Athens for training in the best school available, Plato's Academy, where he would spend the next twenty years. Thus ended the first of the four phases of Aristotle's life.

Life's Work

Aristotle's career divides itself naturally into three periods: the twenty (some say nineteen) years at Plato's Academy, from 368 to 348; the thirteen years of travel, from 348 to 335; and the return to Athens, or the years in the Lyceum, from 335 to 323.

When young Aristotle arrived at the Academy, Plato was away on a second journey to Syracuse. When the master returned the following year, however, Aristotle became his prize student and ardent friend. Although most of Aristotle's earlier works have been preserved only in fragments, usually in quotations within works by later scholars of the Peripatetic School, several are attributed to this period and the one that followed.

Library of Congress

As Plato's method was dialogue, Aristotle, like other students at the Academy, began writing in dialogue. Aristotle was influenced by Plato about the time the master altered his own form, moving toward dialogues other than those with Socrates as questioner and main speaker. Aristotle, in turn, made himself the main speaker in his own dialogues.

Some scholars consider *De anima* the best of Aristotle's works from this period. Translated as *On the Soul*, this work treats the soul and immortality, and is imitative of Plato's *Phaedo*, which was written circa 388-366 B.C. (Critic Werner Jaeger believes that each of Aristotle's early dialogues was influenced by a particular Platonic dialogue, that the student was still dependent on the master as far as metaphysics was concerned but independent in the areas of methodology and logic.) Aristotle's *Protrepticus* (*Protreptics*) is named for a term designating a letter written in defense of philosophy; the method employed in this work (questions and answers by teacher and student) is from Plato, but the protreptic form is borrowed from the philosopher Isocrates, who was also at Athens during this time. In the year 348 (or 347), two events influenced Aristotle's future: the death of Plato (and possibly the choice of a new leader of the Academy), which caused Aristotle to leave Athens, and Philip II's destruction of Stagirus, which caused the philosopher to look elsewhere for a new home.

With a fellow Academic, Xenocrates, Aristotle left Athens for Mysia (modern Turkey), accepting the invitation of Hermeias, a former fellow student at the Academy who had risen from slavery to become ruler of Atarneus and Assos. Aristotle presided over his host's small Platonic circle, making of it a school modeled after the Academy. He married Pythias, niece and adopted daughter of Hermeias, after the ruler's death; they had a daughter, also named Pythias. His wife lived until late in Aristotle's so-called second Athenian period. After three years came another move, this time to Mytilene on the nearby island of Lesbos; it is possible that Theophrastus found him a suitable place of residence there. Having begun research in marine biology at Assos, Aristotle continued this work at Mytilene. During these years, he probably wrote *De philosophia* (*On Philosophy*), *Ethica Eudemia* (*Eudemian Ethics*), and early portions of *Physica* (*Physics*), *Metaphysica* (*Metaphysics*), and *Politica* (*Politics*).

In 343, Aristotle accepted Philip's invitation to move to Pella and become tutor to his thirteen-year-old, Alexander (the Great). The tutoring lasted until Alexander became regent in 340. It is uncertain whether Aristotle remained in Pella or moved to Stagira, which had been rebuilt by Philip in honor of Aristotle. With the assassination of Philip in 335 and the resultant accession of Alexander, Aristotle returned to Athens.

This time Aristotle's purpose was not to attend the Academy but to found its greatest competitor. The Lyceum was situated on rented property just outside the city, since an outsider could not own Athenian land. In addition to the marine specimens Aristotle himself had collected, the school housed many more. It is said that Alexander became his old teacher's benefactor, donating eight hundred talents and instructing all under his command throughout the world to preserve for Aristotle any unusual biological specimens. The site was probably to the northeast of the city, where lay a grave sacred to Apollo Lyceius and the Muses, a place where Socrates had enjoyed walking.

In addition to specimens, the Lyceum housed hundreds of manuscripts and numerous maps. The objects in the museum were used to illustrate Aristotle's lectures and discussions. In the mornings, he utilized the peripatetic (walking) method by strolling through the trees, discussing with more advanced students difficult (esoteric) subjects; in the evenings, he would lecture to larger groups on popular (exoteric) subjects. Logic, physics, and metaphysics were discussed; lectures included rhetoric, sophistic, and politics. In turn, Aristotle seems to have prepared and made available two types of notes: preliminary ones, from which he lectured, and more polished treatises, based on the discussions. Many of these have survived as his later, published works. They are in the form of treatises rather than dialogues.

With the death of Alexander and the rise of feelings in Athens against Macedonians, especially those who had been close to Alexander, Aristotle left Athens for his mother's birthplace of Chalcis, where he died a year later of a disease that had afflicted him for some time.

In his later years at Athens, Aristotle is described as well-dressed, enjoying the easy life of self-indulgence; he was bald and thin-legged with small eyes; he spoke with a lisp and had a mocking disposition and a ready wit. After the death of his wife, he lived with a mistress, Herpyllis, in a permanent but nonlegal relationship. Together, they had a son, whom Aristotle named Nicomachus, after his father.

Summary

Aristotle developed through the earliest stage for about seventeen or eighteen years, moving in circles with doctors and princes. He then spent the next twenty years at the Academy with Plato, both imitating and growing away from his great master. Aristotle learned the method of dialogue while he moved toward his own method; he respected and loved Plato but questioned some Platonic thought, such as the theory of forms (dualistic being). During the next thirteen or fourteen years in Asia Minor, he established a smaller academy and did biological research, continuing the writing of dialogues as he had done at Athens but developing his own method of writing treatises. For three years he was tutor to Alexander, becoming lifelong friends with the future conqueror and ruler of the Mediterranean world but failing to impart his own political views to his student.

When Aristotle returned to Athens to found and preside over the Lyceum, he perfected his scientific method of examining specimens and establishing logical systems of substantiation before arriving at tentative conclusions, a method that has continued to modern times. Through his teaching, he influenced a few advanced students and the large public groups who heard his lectures. Through the Peripatetic School, his work continued for centuries and many of his writings were preserved to influence even later centuries. He learned from and utilized the thought of Greek philosophers from Thales to Plato, extending their ideas and synthesizing them. He perfected the method of Socrates (who had intended such an extension himself) by reaching conclusions rather than probing endlessly. Plato and Aristotle have been more influential than all other Western philosophers, advancing Greek philosophy to its greatest height.

Bibliography

Ackrill, J. L. *Aristotle the Philosopher*. New York: Oxford University Press, 1981. According to this interesting guidebook, "What really characterizes Aristotle as a philosopher is not the number and weight of his conclusions (his 'doctrines'), but the number and power and subtlety of his arguments and ideas and analyses."

Aristotle. *The Works of Aristotle Translated into English Under the Editorship of W. D. Ross*. 12 vols. Oxford: Clarendon Press, 1908-1952. This multivolume text of Aristotle's works, translated over many years, is the recommended version for English-reading students.

Brumbaugh, Robert S. *The Philosophers of Greece*. Albany: State University of New York Press, 1981. This introductory volume traces Greek philosophy from Thales to Socrates, Plato, and Aristotle. Focusing on three important regions—Ionia, southern Italy/Sicily, and Athens—Brumbaugh reviews three questions asked by the Greeks: What is being (what is real)? What am I? and Is there one world or many?

Cantor, Norman F., and Peter L. Klein, eds. *Ancient Thought: Plato and Aristotle*. Vol. 1, *Monuments of Western Thought*. Waltham, Mass.: Blaisdell Publishing Co., 1969. In this volume, contrasts between the two great philosophers are noted.

Ferguson, John. *Aristotle*. Boston: Twayne Publishers, 1972. Assisting the general reader in the study of Aristotle's works, this book presents chapters such as "Life and Times," "The Lost Dialogues," "Philosophy of Nature," "Psychology," and "The Legacy of Aristotle." Part of Twayne's World Authors series.

Fuller, B. A. G. *History of Greek Philosophy: Aristotle*. New York: Henry Holt, 1931. Reprint. New York: Greenwood Press, 1968. Chapter 1 tells of Aristotle's life, while chapters 2 through 11 treat the various phases of his philosophical thought from metaphysics to form and matter, including Aristotelian physics, concern for the unmoved mover, logic, ethics, political thought, rhetoric, and poetics. The final chapter provides a useful review.

Jaeger, Werner. *Aristotle: Fundamentals of the History of His Development*. Translated by Richard Robinson. Oxford: Clarendon Press, 1934, 1948. A translation from the German, this volume attempts to show that Aristotle's views were not static. Jaeger traces Aristotle's development through three life stages—"The Academy," "Travels," and "Maturity"—and treats both biographical data and the works. Here, Aristotle is approached according to the Aristotelian developmental method. A highly recommended source.

Kiernan, Thomas P., ed. *Aristotle Dictionary: With an Introduction by Theodore E. James*. New York: Philosophical Library, 1962. This useful dictionary of Aristotelian terms is preceded by a 157-page introduction outlining the philosopher's life and works. Well-organized and readable.

McKeon, Richard. *Introduction to Aristotle*. New York: Modern Library, 1947. The general introduction is divided into treatments, including the life and times, scientific method in the philosophy, theoretical and practical sciences, and influence. Works and their respective introductions are treated in sections entitled "Logic," "Physics," "Psychology and Biology," "Ethics," "Politics," and "Rhetoric and Poetics."

Ross, Sir David. *Aristotle*. Rev. ed. New York: Barnes and Noble Books, 1949. Following a very detailed overview of the life and works, this source treats the works under the same headings as does McKeon. Much attention is given to whether a work is authentic, Ross often ruling that it is not. This approach contrasts with that of Jaeger, who tends to regard many works as authentic. Includes detailed data regarding Aristotle's successors, citers, and commentators in the main text and in a chronology at the end.

Wilbur, James B., and Harold J. Allen. *The Worlds of Plato and Aristotle*. American Book Co., 1962. This volume treats the philosophies of the two men "as whole perspectives of life and the world by utilizing the actual writings." Plato is the subject of the first half, Aristotle the second. The general introduction to the latter discusses the two men, then Aristotle's method. Numerous selections from the works are discussed and cited under six topics and many subtopics.

George W. Van Devender

RICHARD ARKWRIGHT

Born: December 23, 1732; Preston, Lancashire, England
Died: August 3, 1792; Cromford, Derbyshire, England
Areas of Achievement: Industry and technology
Contribution: Through exceptional drive, organizational ability, and unbounded confidence, Arkwright synthesized cotton spinning by machine into a continuous process under one roof and thereby established the factory system that was to characterize what came to be called the Industrial Revolution.

Early Life

Richard Arkwright was born December 23, 1732, in the northwest of England at Preston, Lancashire. He was the youngest of thirteen children. Only the barest details of his early life are known, an ignorance which the older, successful Arkwright did nothing to dispel. His formal education was slight: His Uncle Richard taught him to read and write. While apprenticed to a barber at Kirkham, a village to the west of Preston, he is said to have attempted to improve on his meager educational skills and even attended a school in the winter months. His apprenticeship completed, Arkwright moved the few miles to Bolton. There, he worked for a wig maker. His early career was marked by attempts to succeed in business for himself. He kept a public house which, after initial success, failed. It is said that at this time he exhibited a genius for mechanics, bleeding (a standard medical therapy of the time), and tooth-drawing; both these latter two talents were taught as part of the traditional barber's trade.

In 1755, Arkwright was married and a son, Richard, was born. What happened to his wife is unclear. He was remarried in 1761. Following his second marriage, Arkwright was able to use his wife's money to set himself up as a traveling merchant. Buying human hair at country fairs from impoverished young women, Arkwright dyed the hair with a process of his own and sold it to commercial wig makers. In this business he achieved quite a measure of success. At that time, Lancashire was full of spinners and weavers working in their own homes. The demand for spun cotton was increasing and, despite certain improvements in the spinning process, the problem of mechanizing spinning remained unresolved. On his travels through the villages and towns, Arkwright heard discussions and speculations surrounding the solution to this pressing problem. So involved in the spinning question did Arkwright become that, by the late 1760's, he was devoting all of his efforts to overcoming the technical difficulties of mechanizing the spinning process. By January, 1768, Arkwright and his paid assistant, the clockmaker John Kay, set up a working model of a spinning machine in Preston. The machine, later known as the water-frame, was not a profoundly original breakthrough, but it was a

Library of Congress

dramatic development. Like many inventors of this period, Arkwright drew heavily on the work of others. He lived at a time and in a place of great technological ferment. Arkwright reworked the ideas of others and came up with a new synthesis of existing ideas which led to a successful machine, in terms of both the quantity of production and the quality of the product.

The character of Richard Arkwright was commented upon by many people. The futile attempts of his own son and of William Nicholson, Secretary of the Chamber of Manufacturers, to compile materials for a biography of the great man a few years after his death demonstrate Arkwright's secrecy and his determination to erase all records of the means by which he acquired such wealth. What is clear is that Arkwright prompted suspicion in his rivals, was generally feared for his aims, and was self-sufficient, domineering, and vulgar. His whole life seemed to be driven by the desire to make money. He generally began work at five in the morning and finished at nine in the evening. He often conducted his business in a coach driven by four powerful, swift horses while traveling between his various factories.

Upon viewing Joshua Wright's famous portrait of Richard Arkwright, Thomas Carlyle, the great nineteenth century English literary critic and liberal, described the industrialist as "a plain, almost gross, bag-cheeked, pot bellied Lancashire man, with an air of painful reflection, yet also of copious free digestion." A close student of Arkwright's career and a near contemporary, Edward Baines, was more substantial in his assessment: "His natural disposition was ardent, enterprising, and stubbornly persevering: His mind was as coarse as it was bold and active, and his manners were rough and unpleasing." In this description, one can see a type which was to become more familiar as machine production spread to other industries and to other countries: the self-made industrialist.

Life's Work

In April, 1768, mindful of the trouble suffered by James Hargreaves, who had been attacked by angry Lancashire cotton spinners afraid of unemployment, Arkwright decided to set up production in Nottingham in the English Midlands, where Hargreaves had found a more tranquil home. There, Arkwright needed increased financial backing and eventually found it in two successful stocking manufacturers, Samuel Need and Jedediah Strutt. The following year, 1769, a patent was granted for Arkwright's new spinning machine, and a small factory was set up in Nottingham to produce cotton thread by means of the machine, powered by horses. Horsepower proved to be too expensive for Arkwright's taste and so, in 1771, with Strutt's backing, Arkwright was enabled to develop his invention on a large scale by building a factory at Cromford, near Derby. The site was somewhat unusual. It was in the middle of nowhere, with no roads or other communications to the outside world and no nearby settlement. Its greatest asset was that it was located on the River Derwent, whose rushing waters could drive Arkwright's machines, henceforth known as water-frames. It was from the use of water power that early factories were often known as mills. In addition, hot springs running into the river above the mill assured that the waters would not freeze in winter. Over the years, Arkwright built up a community around his factory, the first of the cotton villages; he built houses and dormitories, a school, and a church. Roads were built to connect Cromford with Derby and Nottingham.

Armed with his patent for the water-frame, Arkwright sought to expand his business. In 1773, he and his partners set up weaving workshops in Derby. There, for the first time in England, pure cotton cloth, or calico, was produced. The water-frame made it possible. Previously, cotton had been combined with linen, since the method of hand spinning cotton produced a thread of uneven quality and strength. Linen thread was necessary as warp in weaving so as to avoid the problem of constant breakage of cotton thread when put under stress. Arkwright's machine, through its use of pairs of rollers, was able to spin cotton to a uniform fineness and then twist the thread on spindles or flyers to give it strength. The quality of cotton thread was thus greatly improved, strengthened and made more uniform. Demand for the new calico cloth was immediate. At this point, Arkwright faced a serious problem. England's wealth had been built originally upon wool and woolen textiles. The acquisition of India by England had led to competition at home with lighter imported cotton goods. To protect domestic woolen manufactures, Parliament passed an act in 1736 ordering a double duty to be paid on all cotton goods. If Arkwright were to succeed, he would have to secure a change in the law. Despite the opposition of the Lancashire manufacturers, Arkwright's petition to Parliament resulted in a new law, the Calico Act of 1774, which acknowledged the fledgling pure cotton textile industry and swept away all impediments to its development.

Arkwright's overwhelming competitive position in cotton spinning, protected as it was by his patent of 1769, was supplemented in 1775 by the grant of a second patent covering all parts of the spinning process. It caused a furor among other cotton manufacturers, who maintained that Arkwright claimed originality for machinery already in use: a carding machine, crank and comb, roving frame, feeder, and other, minor features. The only originality, it was claimed, lay in Arkwright's arrangement of them into an integrated, powered system operating under one roof. In taking out this patent, Arkwright aimed to obtain a monopoly on spinning machinery and an overwhelming place in spinning output. His monopolistic tendencies were supplemented by plans at various times to buy up the entire world output of cotton; to apply his machinery, acquire new patents, and consequently acquire a monopoly for woolen and worsted spinning; and even, as he boasted, to pay the national debt.

The 1775 patent was, in effect, a declaration of war against the rest of the cotton industry. The Lancashire manufacturers in particular resented the very principle of patents and combined against Arkwright. In an action in the courts in 1781 for patent infringement, Arkwright's case against the Lancashire cotton-mill owner, Colonel Mordaunt, was thrown out, his patent for the carding machine invalidated. Until this time, for a period of six years, Arkwright was able to expand his interests with Strutt, enter partnerships with several others to build more factories in the Midlands and Lancashire, collect royalties from licenses given under his patents, supply the machinery himself to licensees, and buy into their industrial activities. Thus, despite his failure to secure an extension of the water-frame patent beyond 1783 and the loss of his carding patent in 1781, Arkwright was still the richest cotton spinner in England with the most, and the best-run, factories and the ability to set cotton-thread prices for the industry.

Further troubles came from cotton spinners themselves. Machinery threatened the livelihoods of thousands of them. The American Revolution led to a trade depression; many were impoverished and unemployed. The jenny, water-frame, carding machine, and other new machines cut drastically the number of workers needed. The result was that factories, especially in Lancashire, the center of cotton production, were physically attacked and the machines were broken. Among the factories destroyed was Arkwright's at Birkacre, then the largest in Great Britain. Fortunately, trade resumed and the cotton industry surged after 1779.

The campaign to resecure his cotton-spinning patents led Arkwright back into court in 1785. Initially, he was successful. His success so alarmed cotton manufacturers in Lancashire that, led by Sir Robert Peel, father of the future prime minister, they obtained a writ for a new trial. The case against Arkwright, as identified for the jury by Mr. Justice Buller, rested on three points: the originality of his invention, his claim to have developed it himself, and the sufficiency of his official specification of the invention. The two chief prosecution witnesses were John Kay, Arkwright's paid assistant at the time the water-frame was developed, and Thomas Highs, whom Kay asserted was the original inventor. Kay said that he had made models for Highs and later duplicated them when asked by Arkwright. The claims of other inventors for aspects of Arkwright's 1775 patent were also promoted. The special jury found against Arkwright on all three points. Arkwright lost all patent rights.

A lesser man would have been crushed by the four years of patent fights. Arkwright was undaunted. At the end of 1783, Arkwright financed Samuel Oldknow, who was to become the foremost muslin manufacturer in England. From 1784, Arkwright's Scottish interests were firmly established: He helped finance the cotton mills of David Dale at New Lanark (whose son-in-law and successor was Robert Owen, the famous industrial reformer and Socialist) and mills in Perthshire and Ayrshire. In addition, Arkwright continued to build new mills of his own, expand existing ones, and replenish machinery in the light of the latest improvements. In 1790, Arkwright began to apply steam power to his works with a Boulton and Watt engine at his Nottingham factory. Thereafter, the water-frame driven by steam power came to be called a throstle.

In 1786, Arkwright was knighted after he delivered a loyal address to George III upon the King's escape from assassination. The following year, he was made High Sheriff of Derbyshire, an unusual honor for a man in trade. He apparently carried out his duties with flamboyance. His elegant coach was accompanied by thirty javelin men in sumptuous livery, and he provided great banquets during the period of the assize (a major regional law court). Like many successful merchants and later manufacturers, Arkwright invested in personal loans and land. In 1789, he purchased the manor of Cromford, beginning the erection of a church for his workers and a castle for himself. He died of complications related to his lifelong subjection to asthma, leaving his castle still unfinished.

Summary

Much speculation has surrounded Richard Arkwright's development of the water-frame. The language used to describe it and his other inventions in both patent descriptions was deliberately vague and misleading. Other names have been put forward as the true originators of the various spinning machines claimed by Arkwright. The patent trials of 1781 and 1785 brought forth accusations taken up by later writers. Whatever the truth may be, and there is considerable doubt concerning Arkwright's mechanical originality, he is a seminal figure in the history of the Industrial Revolution. After the patent trials when he had testified on Arkwright's behalf, James Watt commented,

> As to Mr. Arkwright, he is, to say no worse, one of the most self-sufficient, ignorant men I have ever met with, yet, by all I can learn, he is certainly a man of merit in his way, and one to whom Britain is much indebted, and whom she should honour and reward, for whoever invented the spinning machine, Arkwright certainly had the merit of performing the most difficult part, which was the making it useful.

From the late 1770's until his death, despite his clashes with the Manchester Committee of Trade over patent rights, Arkwright led the cotton industry. Indeed, in 1788, Arkwright's name headed the trade's fight against its most serious rival, the powerful East India Company. Arkwright's factory communities, with their twenty-four-hour production schedules, twelve-hour work shifts, massive employment of children, poor ventilation, paternalism, and work incentives (which included bonuses, distinctive clothing for prize workers, and annual celebrations), had been copied by numerous others by the end of the eighteenth century. His factory organization served as a model well into the nineteenth century. To Sir Edward Baines, Arkwright "possessed very high inventive talent, as well as an unrivalled sagacity in estimating at their true value the mechanical contrivances of others, in combining them together, perfecting them, arranging a complete series of machinery, and constructing the factory system—itself a vast and admirable machine, which has been the source of great wealth, both to individuals and to the nation." Finally, according to Paul Mantoux, the great historian of the Industrial Revolution, Arkwright "personified the new type of the great manufacturer, neither an engineer nor a merchant, but adding to the main characteristics of both, qualifications peculiar to himself: those of a founder of great concerns, an organizer of production and a leader of men. Arkwright's career heralded a new social class and a new economic era."

Bibliography

Baines, Sir Edward. *History of the Cotton Manufacture in Great Britain*. London: H. Fisher, R. Fisher, and P. Jackson, 1835. Reprint. New York: Augustus M. Kelley, 1966. Originally published in 1835; its frontispiece is the famous portrait which inspired Carlyle. The first few chapters give a history of cotton from ancient times. Very informative about inventions, Arkwright (chapter 9), and the development of the industry. A major source for subsequent works.

Daniels, George W. *The Early English Cotton Industry*. Manchester: Manchester University Press, 1920. Good background treatment, especially concerned with Crompton's weaving breakthrough. Chapters 3 and 4 deal substantially with Arkwright.

Deane, Phyllis. *The First Industrial Revolution*. 2d ed. Cambridge: Cambridge University Press, 1979. One of the standard works on the causes, course, and consequences of the Industrial Revolution. Chapter 6 deals with the cotton industry and Arkwright's part in it.

Fitton, R. S., and A. B. Wadsworth. *The Strutts and the Arkwrights, 1758-1830*. Manchester: Manchester University Press, 1958. Reconstructed largely from Strutt family letters and the business records of the Strutt company. Full of valuable insight and direct quotation concerning this important partnership dissolved in 1783. Relations between the Arkwright and Strutt families were very close for many years afterward. Contains the best account of Arkwright's life and contains much valuable insight into Arkwright's business behavior.

Guest, Richard. *A Compendious History of the Cotton Manufacture: With a Disproval of the Claim of Sir Richard Arkwright to the Invention of Its Ingenious Machinery*. J. Pratt, 1823. Reprint. New York: Augustus M. Kelley, 1968. Advances the claim of Thomas Highs to authorship both of the water-frame and of the spinning jenny. Excellent quotations from the

1785 patent trial and wonderful sketches of the various mechanical inventions. Arkwright was successful, the author claims, only because he made the clockmaker John Kay drunk and stole the invention.

Mantoux, Paul. *The Industrial Revolution in the Eighteenth Century: An Outline of the Beginnings of the Modern Factory System in England*. Translated by Marjorie Vernon. New York: Harcourt, Brace and Co., 1927. Reprint. Chicago: University of Chicago Press, 1983. Published originally in French (1906), then English (1927), and revised in 1961, this work is, in many ways, unsurpassed as an account of the Industrial Revolution. Well written and very insightful regarding Arkwright and much else.

Thompson, E. P. *The Making of the English Working Class*. New York: Vintage Books, 1966. The classic account of the human cost of the Industrial Revolution and the very active role in attempting to shape their lives played by the newly forming class of industrial workers. Contains the best account of the reasons behind machine-breaking. Highly readable and highly recommended.

Unwin, George. *Samuel Oldknow and the Arkwrights: The Industrial Revolution in Stockport and Marple*. Manchester: Manchester University Press, 1924. A model business history drawn mainly from voluminous records discovered by chance in Oldknow's factory, long abandoned following a fire. Very good for the business correspondence of Arkwright and his market position. Arkwright financed Oldknow, who became England's foremost muslin manufacturer. In the complete absence of any business records of Arkwright himself, this and Fitton and Wadsworth's work on the Strutts is the closest the student may come to the business methods of Arkwright.

Wadsworth, A. B., and J. de L. Mann. *The Cotton Trade and Industrial Lancashire, 1600-1780*. Manchester: Manchester University Press, 1931. Very good for the context of Arkwright's career and the incremental nature of technological change.

Stephen Burwood

EDWIN H. ARMSTRONG

Born: December 18, 1890; New York, New York
Died: January 31, 1954; New York, New York
Area of Achievement: Radio electronics
Contribution: From the infancy of radio, Armstrong was the leading edge of its technical development, inventing the basic circuitry of modern AM-FM broadcasting.

Early Life

Edwin Howard Armstrong was born on December 18, 1890, to a middle-class New York City family. His youth was a reflection of America's fascination with the revolutionary technical innovations then transforming the nation's society. As a boy, Armstrong displayed a markedly precocious ability with things mechanical and developed a strong interest in trains and locomotives. He read voraciously of the then-popular Horatio Alger "Rags to Riches" adventure books for boys as well as the new science-fiction stories. He declared in later life that his career in science began at fourteen, when, after reading about the exploits of inventor Guglielmo Marconi, he decided to become an inventor himself. Fabricating his own coherers, detectors, and hand-wound coils, he had, by his mid-teens, built his own spark-based station for listening to wireless broadcasts. Radio had become his consuming interest by the time he entered Columbia University to study electrical engineering. While working there in the graduate radio laboratory, he was exposed to Lee de Forest's then-recent invention of the Audion, or three-element vacuum tube. Although de Forest had at that time used the tube only for the amplification of audio signals, Armstrong immediately saw the possibility of using the tube to generate radio frequency signals, and in a short time he developed the regenerative or feedback amplification circuit. Because he was unable to persuade his father to fund a prompt patent application, his claim for the invention was delayed until January, 1913, when a drawing of the regenerative circuit was notarized. By this time, de Forest had realized this important application of the Audion tube and filed his own patent, followed by Alexander Meissner in Germany and C. S. Franklin in England.

Thus, when Armstrong was graduated from Columbia University in May, 1913, he found himself embroiled in an international dispute over patent rights to a major invention, defending his position against some of the greatest names in radio. This legal dispute over patent rights was the beginning of a pattern that would follow him for the remainder of his life.

Life's Work

Armstrong's time during his twenties was spent in bitter litigation with de

Smithsonian Institution

Forest, and although de Forest eventually won the patent, de Forest continued the deep animosity between the men by maintaining interference proceedings for the next ten years.

During World War I, Armstrong served in Paris as a United States Signal Corps officer attached to the radio laboratory of the École Militaire. By his later account, he was there struck by the difficulty of building triode amplifiers capable of intercepting the extremely weak, shortwave signals then used by the Germans in their field communications. The amplifiers in use could not sustain the power levels required without breaking into self-driven oscillation from unwanted feedback.

Armstrong's solution was to convert the incoming signal to a fixed frequency by heterodyning them to a local oscillator in the receiver and obtaining the needed sensitivity by processing the signal at the lower imposed frequency, where stability was more readily secured. It was an elegant design and has proved basic to all later receiver circuitry. In the summer of 1920, after additional research at Columbia University, he was awarded the United States patent for the superheterodyne receiver circuit.

Although he possessed the most fundamental receiver and transmitter patents, Armstrong's position was by no means secure. His patent for the regenerative circuit was under attack by de Forest in the U.S. Patent Office, incurring heavy legal expenses. In the fall of 1920, he sold the superheterodyne receiver patent to Westinghouse for $335,000 in cash, with an additional $200,000 to be paid if he won the interference proceedings against de Forest.

While setting up a courtroom demonstration in 1921, he noticed an unusual mode of radio detection and, following experimental development, filed patent application for the superregenerative detector, which was awarded in 1922.

In 1924, his patent for the superheterodyne circuit was challenged by the American Telephone and Telegraph Company (AT&T), which possessed the American rights to the patent of Lucien Levy, a French radio engineer. Levy claimed to have invented the superheterodyne receiver during the war while stationed at the École Militaire and that Armstrong had stolen the invention while serving there in the signal corps.

Armstrong spent his energy and personal financial resources defending the patent position in the courts against bitter professional and sometimes personal attacks. Although he retained rights to the regenerative circuits, he ultimately lost all the claims for the superheterodyne circuit to Levy, backed by AT&T.

During these legal battles, from 1928 to 1933, he developed, with little assistance, his finest invention, the wideband frequency modulation (FM) system of broadcasting, proving a static and distortion-free technique, far superior to AM. In the winter of 1933, he was awarded four patents which completely covered the FM system and which established him as its sole inventor. As the newly appointed professor of electrical engineering at Columbia University, he announced his invention to the world by reading a paper before the Institute of Radio Engineers and surprising his audience with a demonstration broadcast from an experimental station he operated with the help of a friend. His system was obviously superior to any AM system in use, yet its introduction was met with the skepticism of industry, which had invested heavily in AM broadcasting. Much of the remainder of his life was spent in trying to have FM adopted as the prime radio broadcasting system. He refined the techniques, set up stations, and traveled extensively, but with little result.

During World War II, he developed FM units for military communications, demonstrated long-range FM signaling, and worked on continuous-wave FM radar.

Harassed by seemingly never-ending patent litigation and frustrated by the slow adoption of his FM broadcasting system, Armstrong committed suicide in New York on January 31, 1954.

Summary

Edwin Armstrong's career spanned the golden age of radio development and broadcasting and reflected the spirit of the individual scientific pioneer that was typical of the early twentieth century. His work, from his undergraduate days, was always on the very basic phenomena of radio operations, his early contributions making possible the dream of voice radio transmission.

Much of his energy in the later years of his life was spent fighting challenges to his patents. If this time could have been devoted to invention and research, his scientific output could have been much higher. Despite this drain on him, he invented some of the most important circuits of modern radio, his creative output spanning the whole of his career.

Although he died feeling frustrated and unrecognized, the world has since seen the adoption of his systems as the standard of broadcasting and his ranking as one of the great scientists of modern electronics. His awards include the First Medal of Honor from the Society of Radio Engineers, the Franklin Medal, and the United States Medal of Merit. He is one of twenty world scientists honored in the Pantheon of the Union Internationale des Télécommunications in Geneva.

Bibliography

Aitken, Hugh G. *The Conlinous Wave: Technology and American Radio, 1900-1932*. Princeton, N.J.: Princeton University Press, 1985. The best history of the development of radio available. Covers Armstrong's patent and business dealings in depth as well as his impact on the development of the Radio Corporation of America (RCA), and Westinghouse as the dominant companies of early radio. Very well researched and documented, both historically and technically.

___________. *Syntony and Spark: The Origins of Radio*. New York: John Wiley and Sons, 1976. An excellent chronological history of the technical evolution of radio. Gives a broad picture of Armstrong's technical innovations and how they affected the rapid pace of radio's development at the time.

Lessing, Lawrence. *Man of High Fidelity: Edwin Howard Armstrong*. Philadelphia: J. B. Lippincott Co., 1956. The only biography yet written on the life of Armstrong, and the only source for information on his private life. Well written but sympathetic toward Armstrong's difficulties. Provides a more personable view of the legal charges and accusations against Armstrong.

Lewis, Thomas S. W. "Radio Revolutionary." *American Heritage of Invention and Technology* 1 (Fall, 1985): 34-41. A sympathetic but accurate brief account contrasting his tragic life with his triumphant inventions, especially FM.

Orren P. Whiddon

ARNOLD OF VILLANOVA

Born: c. 1239; Valencia, Spain? or Provence region, France?
Died: 1311; Genoa, Italy
Areas of Achievement: Medicine and religion
Contribution: The first great figure of European medicine, physician to kings and popes, Arnold joined Arabic theory to European empiricism. His more than seventy scientific works and translations made him an influential medical theorist down past the sixteenth century, just as his radical theology and stormy life made him lastingly controversial.

Early Life

France, Italy, and Spain have claimed Arnold as a native son. "Villanova" may derive from Villeneuve-les-Vence, or else Villeneuve-Loubet, in Provence, where he had relatives. By one theory, his family were Jews who, on converting to Christianity, moved to Catalonia and then Valencia. Arnold himself said that he was "born of the soil, lowly and obscure" and called himself "an unlearned country-fellow." Contemporaries called him a Catalan, which he accepted, and his early editors used that as an alternate surname. The only language in which he wrote, besides Latin, was Catalan. The kingdom of Valencia, just conquered from the Muslims by Catalonia-Aragon, always claimed Arnold for its own. The great fourteenth century Valencian writer Francesc Eiximenis took it as common knowledge, within a lifetime of Arnold's death, that the latter was a native of Valencia. The settlers in Valencia, and even those in Murcia to its south, were called "true Catalans" by the contemporary memoirist Ramón Muntaner; famous medieval Valencians such as Vicent Ferrer and the Borgia popes, as well as the Majorcan Anselm Turmeda, were also called Catalans. Thus, Arnold was probably born in Valencia, after the fall of its capital in 1238. Arnold had properties in Valencia and, more significant, was ordained as a cleric in minor orders in the Valencian diocese; his daughter Maria became a nun at Valencia city in 1291.

In 1982, John Benton published a note from a medieval manuscript archived in Pasadena, California, indicating that Arnold was born at Villanueva de Jilóca near Huesca in Aragon and that some of his relatives still lived there in the mid-fourteenth century. Benton suggested that Arnold learned his Arabic from the conquered Muslims there and was an Aragonese by early training. There is no evidence, however, that Arnold knew any Aragonese, while he is a major figure in Catalan literature. Moreover, it is unlikely that Aragon's acculturated Muslim farming communities, with their Arabic dialect, were the source of his classical Arabic and his knowledge of its literature. Valencia was an advanced Islamic society, barely come under colonial rule, with its Muslim aristocracy, savants, and schools intact during

New York Academy of Medicine

the long decades of Arnold's education. As a Valencian, Arnold's environment would have been multiethnic, among affluent Muslim and Jewish communities in a land of international ports, lush farmlands, and dangerous revolts on the part of the Muslim majority—a far cry from the bleak and rocky uplands of Aragon.

Life's Work

Arnold of Villanova (Arnau de Vilanova in his native Catalan) was graduated around 1260 from the celebrated medical university in Montpellier, then part of the wider realms of Aragon-Catalonia. He may have done postdoctoral work at Naples under the physician Giovanni de Casamicciola. Presumably during his Montpellier sojourn, he married Agnès Blasi of that city, herself of a lineage of physicians. In the early 1280's, he studied Hebrew and the Talmud under the Arabist-Hebraist Ramón Martí at the Dominican school in Barcelona. Famous by 1281, Arnold became the main physician to King Peter III of Aragon-Catalonia, receiving the huge stipend of two thousand Barcelonan sous on condition of living in Barcelona near the court (another indication that his home was not Catalonia but Valencia). Other gifts included the castle of Ollers. Arnold continued to enjoy royal support under Peter's successors, Alfonso III (reigned 1285-1291) and James II (reigned 1291-1327), and he was released to reside in Valencia, which he did from 1286 to 1289.

Called to teach at Montpellier for a decade, Arnold began to publish apocalyptic religious works, prophesying the coming of Antichrist in 1345 (later revised to 1368) and demanding moral reform. When James II sent the respected doctor on a diplomatic mission to Philip IV of France, Arnold spread his radical theology so passionately that the theologians of the University of Paris had him tried and condemned in 1299. Pope Boniface VIII and King Philip secured his release. Grateful for Arnold's cure of his renal affliction, the pope lent him the castle of Scorcola near Anagni as a retreat in which to study and write. Arnold returned to his post with the royal family in 1302. He soon became embroiled in a theological battle with the Dominicans of Gerona and Castellón de Ampurias, and he disputed before the archbishop at Lérida and the king at Barcelona. At Valencia, his polemics prompted the Inquisition to excommunicate him. His patient and protector Boniface VIII died in 1303, but the new pope (Benedict XI, whom Arnold treated for gallstones) shielded him. Further religious polemic got Arnold imprisoned briefly at Perugia in Italy. Under the protection of Frederick III of Sicily, however, he continued his religious writings at Messina.

In 1305, Arnold returned to Barcelona to exhort James II to crusade against Islamic Almería. Continuing to write on medical and religious topics, and by now the European leader of the visionary evangelical movement called the Spirituals, Arnold went to Narbonne and Marseilles; in 1308, he was in Messina, where he interpreted an obsessive dream for King Frederick. In 1309, he was at the court of his friend and patient Pope Clement V in Avignon; in 1310, he was back with Frederick III briefly and in the siege of Almería and then at Messina again. Journeying by sea to Avignon, he died near Genoa and was buried there in 1311. During all these travels, he had enthusiastically propagated the astrological, alchemical, and occult themes then popular in Islam. His method of exegesis by symbolic letters, borrowed from the Jewish Cabalists, disturbed some contemporaries. Suspected of converting to Judaism, he was in reality an anti-Judaic proselytizer. In 1316, the Inquisition at Tarragona condemned a number of his religious approaches. At the same time, he was hailed internationally as a great physician.

In later medieval Mediterranean Europe (as distinguished from the inland and northern regions), a physician was a prestigious personage, expected to be a general savant, a repository of philosophical and even theological ancient knowledge, and also a man active in public affairs. He was a welcome decoration in the courts of the powerful. This model echoes the Islamic *hakim*, extending to the Jews with Arabist training who functioned at the court of the kings of Aragon-Catalonia. Training of physicians in Europe, though often still accomplished through private apprenticeship, had become a university function, so that the university title "doctor" and the renown of the universities themselves were reflecting more glory on the profession. Seen in this light, Arnold's almost comic embroilment in the Spirituals' cause makes more sense; it was then the premier public polemic in Europe. Arnold's diplomatic projects are also thus explained. He never lost sight, however, of his own priorities: He was a physician, in an era of revolutionary advances in surgery, anatomy, and the professionalization of medical work.

Arnold's medical theory has been summed up as "Galen Arabicized." He not only translated Arabic medical works into Latin, including those of the Valencian Abu Salt, but also revered the classic Muslim physicians and integrated their findings with Western medical knowledge and practice. His *Aphorismi de gradibus* (aphorisms on the degrees), done in the late 1290's, revolutionized the study of pharmacology with its theory of compound medicines and its application of mathematics. It organized traditional knowledge into one unified field, while rejecting previous forms of classification. Arnold composed some seventy medical books and treatises in Latin, over a wide range of topics. His work on preventive medicine and hygiene, *Regimen sanitatis* (1307; management of health), enjoyed great popular success; the Queen of Aragon ordered a version translated into Romance for wider diffusion, and a Hebrew version appeared. In all, Arnold wrote eleven such books. He also wrote a book titled *De conservatione juventutis et retardatione senectutis* (1290; *The Conservation of Youth and Defense of Age*, 1544). Other works specialized in bleeding, fevers, poisons, sexual intercourse, conception, sterility, dreams, food for the sick, eye troubles, epilepsy, wines, waters, antidotes, leprosy and contagious diseases, the heart, meat-eating, and medical theory. He discoursed on the value of bathing, kinds of baths, and their effects. He also took up questions on surgery, an art being revolutionized by the treatise of Abulcassis (al-Zahrawi) that he had translated and by pioneering theories on disease as anatomically focused.

The historian of Spanish medieval medicine Luis García Ballester sees Arnold as a frontier phenomenon, a fusion of Arabic, Jewish, and European medical traditions which flowered until supplanted by the Scholastic model of the Italians. Arnold was an academician, and his talent was for joining practice to theory. A catalog of his library survives, affording insights into his intellectual tastes. He was not interested, for example, in Islamic theology. He collected not only Arabic books but also works in Greek, a language he learned only late in life.

Summary

Arnold was the greatest physician in the West since ancient Rome. Physician and spiritual adviser to four kings, physician to three popes, and for a decade the most celebrated teacher at Europe's greatest medical university, Montpellier, Arnold was a tireless author and translator of medical works. More than any medieval figure, he represents the juncture of Arabic with European medicine, theory with practice. At the same time, he was a major figure in public affairs, from diplomatic missions to crusade propaganda; he became the leader of the apocalyptic Spirituals movement then agitating Europe. His writings show his contribution to the evolution of the Catalan language and literature. He had close associations with the Jewish community in southern France, partly to borrow cabalistic knowledge and partly with proselytizing intent. His incessant travel, and the explosive energies visible both in his production of books and in the disputations which made him leader of the Spirituals (and landed him in prison several times), made him one of the best-known public men of his age.

Bibliography

Arnold of Villanova. *Arnaldi de Villanova: Opera Medica Omnia*. Vols. 2 and 16. Edited with introductions by Michael R. McVaugh. Granada, Spain: Seminarium Historiae Medicae Granatensis, 1975. Despite the work's Latin title and edited text, and its Spanish printer, the introductions to these volumes are in English, by the major authority on Arnold. The second volume, *Aphorismi de gradibus*, has 143 pages in English on Arnold's contribution to medieval pharmacology.

Benton, John F. "The Birthplace of Arnau de Vilanova: A Case for Villanueva de Jilóca near Daroca." In *Viator: Medieval and Renaissance Studies*, vol. 13. Berkeley: University of California Press, 1982. The most exciting contribution to the study of Arnold's early years, though controversial in its interpretation. Contains additional information on his career and a bibliography in notes.

Burns, Robert I. "The Medieval Crossbow as Surgical Instrument: An Illustrated Case History." *Bulletin of the New York Academy of Medicine* 48 (September, 1972): 983-989. Reprinted as chapter 7 of Burns's *Moors and Crusaders in Mediterranean Spain* (London: Variorum, 1978). Six thirteenth century panels illustrate a surgical procedure, including the preparation of the patient beforehand by assistants and the formal dress of physicians. The case is explained from contemporary surgical manuals, with relevant bibliography. The site was Elche in the Kingdom of Valencia; the time was Arnold's young manhood.

McVaugh, Michael R. "Quantified Medical Theory and Practice at Fourteenth-Century Montpellier." *Bulletin of the History of Medicine* 43 (September/October, 1969): 397-413. An early presentation of themes expanded by McVaugh in his later introduction to Arnold's works (see above) on mathematical formulas applied to compound medicines.

Siraisi, Nancy G. *Taddeo Alderotti and His Pupils: Two Generations of Italian Medical Learning*. Princeton, N.J.: Princeton University Press, 1981. Though it does not deal with Arnold, this work gives the best introduction in English to the new medicine of the thirteenth century, a panoramic and profound examination of a Mediterranean region then vying with Arnold's Montpellier and Catalonia. Its extensive bibliography includes all the important background books and articles.

Robert I. Burns

SVANTE AUGUST ARRHENIUS

Born: February 19, 1859; Castle of Vik, near Uppsala, Sweden
Died: October 2, 1927; Stockholm, Sweden
Areas of Achievement: Chemistry and physics
Contribution: Arrhenius was one of the founders of the interdisciplinary science of physical chemistry. He also aided in establishing the international reputation of the Nobel Prizes, clarified the physical effects of light pressure from the sun, and developed the conception, called "panspermia," that life was introduced on Earth by spores from space.

Early Life

Svante August Arrhenius was born February 19, 1859, at the castle of Vik, near Uppsala, Sweden. His family had engaged in farming for several generations and had also produced some members of at least modest accomplishment. One relative had written published hymns, an uncle was a scholar, and Arrhenius' own father had attended the University of Uppsala briefly and held a responsible position as superintendent of grounds for the university.

From an early age, Arrhenius showed skill in calculating, and at the Cathedral School in Uppsala he displayed some ability in mathematics and physics. In 1876, at the age of seventeen, Arrhenius enrolled at the University of Uppsala, the oldest and best-known Swedish institution. There to study physics, he ultimately discovered that his instructors were overly committed to experimental topics and were either unaware of or opposed to the rapid developments in theoretical physics. Thus, in 1881 he moved to Stockholm to study with Erik Edlund. By 1884, Arrhenius submitted his doctoral dissertation to the University of Uppsala, but his talent was largely unrecognized and he was granted the lowest possible honor above an outright rejection.

His thesis, built upon the work of Michael Faraday and Sir Humphry Davy, described an effective experimental method for determining the electrical conductivity of compounds in extremely dilute solutions. The thesis also included a preliminary outline of a theory of electrolytic conductivity, in which Arrhenius claimed that the salt was dissociated into two ions in the solution. This ionization increased the number of particles in a given volume, allowing Arrhenius to explain the high osmotic pressures found by Jacobus Hendricus van't Hoff as well as the decreased freezing points and increased boiling points of solutions.

Professor Per Teodor Cleve established the initial response toward Arrhenius' work by ignoring it, presuming that it was no more significant than other student theories. Fortunately, Wilhelm Ostwald recognized the significance of the work and its foundational nature for subsequent developments in the theory of electrolysis.

The Nobel Foundation

Life's Work

Arrhenius, disappointed by the reception of his work, began a campaign to win acceptance by sending copies of his dissertation to several scholars throughout Europe. His work was favorably received by Sir William Ramsay in England and Ostwald in Russia. When Ostwald came to Sweden to visit, his influence secured a lectureship for Arrhenius at Uppsala in 1884 and a travel grant from the Swedish Academy of Sciences in 1886 so that Arrhenius could study further in Europe.

From 1886 to 1891, Arrhenius worked with some of the finest physicists of Europe, including Ostwald in Riga and later in Leipzig, Friedrich Kohlrausch in Würzburg, Ludwig Boltzmann in Graz, and van't Hoff in Amsterdam. During this time, the ionization theory met with extensive resistance. Incomplete atomic theory contributed to the difficulty of accounting for the formation and stable existence of the ions, and certain strong solutions remained anomalous, but Ostwald advocated the fruitfulness of the new theory, demonstrating that it could account for a wide variety of chemical phenomena. When Ostwald joined with van't Hoff to found *Zeitschrift für physikalische Chemie*, Arrhenius took advantage of the opportunity to publish a revised version of his theory of electrolytic dissociation in the first issue. The three close friends thus formed a formidable association promoting the theory.

In 1891, Arrhenius refused a professorship at Giessen, Germany, to become a lecturer at the Högskola, the technical high school in Stockholm, an institution devoted to teaching research methodology in a free form without degrees. Although an outstanding faculty did genuinely creative work, the school was always underequipped. Despite opposition, Arrhenius became a professor in 1895 and later a rector. He and other leaders sought to surpass Uppsala and in the process transformed the Högskola into the University of Stockholm. Beginning in 1898, he was active in formulating the procedures governing the Nobel Prizes and served on the physics committee from 1900 to 1927.

During these years, Arrhenius continued research in electrolytic conductivity, the viscosity of solutions, the effects of temperature upon reaction velocity, and atmospheric conductivity. The results of his research appeared in *Lärobok i teoretisk elektrokemi* (1900; *Text-book of Electrochemistry*, 1902); in 1903, he published *Lehrbuch der kosmischen Physik* (treatise on cosmic physics). Also during this period, Arrhenius' interdisciplinary interests continued to expand. In 1902 and 1903, he studied in Denmark and Germany, working on physiological problems in serum therapy. In 1904, he delivered lectures at the University of California on principles of physical chemistry applied to toxins and antitoxins. In 1905, he refused the offer of a professorship and a private laboratory in Berlin in order to become the director of the Nobel Institute for Physical Chemistry, near Stockholm, a post he held until his death twenty-two years later.

Settling in Stockholm, Arrhenius began an intense period of writing. In 1906, his California lectures appeared as *Theorien der Chemie* (*Theories of Chemistry*, 1907) and as *Immunochemistry* (1907). That year, cosmologists also became aware of him through *Das Werden der Welten*, a German translation of *Världarnas utveckling* (1906; *Worlds in the Making*, 1908). The second law of thermodynamics seemed to many physicists and astronomers to point to the heat death of the universe. Arrhenius sought to discount heat exhaustion with a self-renewing model of the universe in which burned out solar objects were replaced by new stars arising from nebulas that were increasing in temperature.

In this intense period of labor, Arrhenius also published *Människan inför världsgåtan* (1907; *The Life of the Universe as Conceived by Man from Earliest Ages to the Present Time*, 1909), which represented a different approach to the older plurality of worlds (life on other planets) debate. Arrhenius supported other scientists who argued that life was universally diffused throughout the universe from already inhabited planets that gave out spores that were spread through space and reached planets that had evolved to a habitable state. Arrhenius intended this as an alternative to William Thomson's claim that meteorites were the means of seeding the planets with life. These proposals have since been given the descriptive name panspermia, and while they were high in explanatory value they have held little interest since the discovery of intense ultraviolet radiation in space.

Honors came to Arrhenius as the quality of his research was recognized. He was finally elected to the Swedish Academy of Sciences in 1901, and the widespread acceptance of his theory was recognized in 1903, when he was awarded the Nobel Prize in Chemistry. In 1902, he received the Davy Medal of the Royal Society of London and became an associate of the German Chemical Society. On a visit to the United States in 1911, he received the first Willard Gibbs Medal and became an associate of the American Academy of Sciences. In addition, he became a foreign member of the Royal Society in 1911, received the Faraday Medal of the Chemical Society in 1914, and was awarded numerous honorary doctorates.

Throughout his career, Arrhenius continued to conduct research and write. He delivered the 1911 Silliman Lectures at Yale, which were published as *Theories of Solutions* (1912). In 1915, he made a second contribution to biochemistry with *Quantitative Laws in Biological Chemistry*, and in 1918 *The Destinies of the Stars* appeared in English. Despite Arrhenius' confidence in the existence of life throughout the universe, he refrained from excesses and took Percival Lowell to task for imagining more than could be proved. In 1926, Arrhenius published his last major effort, *Erde und Weltall*, a revision and combination of his earlier books on cosmology. He died on October 2, 1927.

Summary

Ironically, Svante August Arrhenius is now most frequently cited for one of his least enduring ideas, that of life originating on planets as the result of panspermia. He is less well known for his more significant accomplishments as a founder of physical chemistry. His reach across disciplinary lines contributed to a fruitful period of research in both physics and chemistry. He strongly wished to internationalize Swedish scientific activity and saw the Nobel Prizes as a means of accomplishing this goal. His role in writing the regulations governing the administration and awarding of these prizes contributed greatly to establishing them as the most significant international scientific award. Offering a satisfactory explanation of the aurora borealis and establishing the existence of light pressure from the sun were his enduring contributions to atmospheric physics and astronomy. His good humor and command of languages (German, French, and English) made him popular wherever scholars gathered and won for him an enduring place in the memories of those with whom he worked.

Bibliography

Crawford, Elisabeth. *The Beginnings of the Nobel Institution: The Science Prizes, 1901-1915*. New York: Cambridge University Press, 1984. This significant scholarly work presents a comprehensive and detailed account of the early history of the science prizes. It also gives extensive detail of Arrhenius' involvement in the organizing of the prizes and his actions in promoting and blocking particular recipients.

Farber, Eduard. *The Evolution of Chemistry.* New York: Ronald Press, 1952. While providing minimal biographical information, this book contains a brief but clear explanation of Arrhenius' theory of dissociation. This theory was Arrhenius' most original work and the foundation of his receiving the Nobel Prize; therefore, this remains a useful source.

__________, ed. *Great Chemists*. New York: Interscience, 1961. This work contains an abridgment and translation of an earlier work on Arrhenius. It is thorough, accurate, and one of the more authoritative English sources. As with most of the available biographical material concerning Arrhenius, there is very little about his private life in the English abridgment, a shortcoming of the book since it tends to decontextualize Arrhenius' place in the science of the day.

Jaffe, Bernard. *Crucibles: The Story of Chemistry.* New York: Simon & Schuster, 1948. One chapter of this book contains a popular and dramatic account of Arrhenius' career, depicting him as a hero who overcame great opposition from entrenched science to receive the recognition that he deserved.

Larson, Cedric A. "Svante August Arrhenius." *Science Digest* 46 (August, 1959): 83-89. This is a readily available, brief, and accurate biography.

Since this is a popular account of his life, the explanations of the science with which Arrhenius was involved are simple. The account of his life is somewhat more personal than the other available sources.

Ivan L. Zabilka

ARYABHATA

Born: A.D. 475 or 476; Kusumapura, India
Died: c. A.D. 550; place unknown
Areas of Achievement: Mathematics and astronomy
Contribution: Aryabhata, the first great Hindu mathematician-astronomer, in 499 wrote *The Aryabhatiya*, which describes the axial rotation of Earth and presents many innovative rules of arithmetic and planar and spherical trigonometry, and solutions to quadratic equations.

Early Life

Aryabhata was born in 475 or 476 at Kusumapura, also known as the City of Flowers, a small town on the Jumna River near its confluence with the Ganges River. Aryabhata's hometown was not far from Pataliputra (now called Patna). Parts of Pataliputra, including Aśoka the Great's ancient royal palace, had been falling into ruins since Candra Gupta II moved the imperial seat from there some seventy-five years before. Pataliputra, a major center of astrology, mythology, and religion, presented a special problem for the scientist. Buddha, tradition held, crossed the Ganges there and prophesied the future greatness of the city, which supposedly had been founded by Putraka, knight of the magic cup, staff, and slippers, and his princess, Patali. In developing his scientific theories, Aryabhata had to contend with these mythological beliefs and popularly held ideas that Earth was flat and that certain heavenly bodies, called *asuras*, were nonluminous, invisible, and demoniac. Although Aryabhata rejected these ideas, astrologers stubbornly clung to them for centuries after his death. It is ironic that Aryabhata lived in Pataliputra and not six hundred miles away in Ujjain in Central India, where science and astronomy, and not religion and astrology, prevailed: Aryabhata's achievements outshone those of any of the scientists at Ujjain at that time and he would later receive recognition as the first of the great Hindu mathematician-astronomers.

Aryabhata, despite the geographic distance from the scientists at Ujjain, was clearly influenced by their style of writing. He, like they, wrote in verse and often presented a mathematical problem in the form of a story, suitable for reading at social occasions. Indeed, at the time, intellectuals would publicly challenge one another to create and solve difficult mathematical problems. Aryabhata also followed the common practice of writing in two different scientific realms. Like many other important Hindu scientists, including the later Brahmagupta (c. 598-c. 660) and Bhāskara (1115-1185), Aryabhata explored both mathematics and astronomy; they all considered themselves primarily astronomers and believed that mathematics was useful only in solving astronomical questions. Also like the other Hindu writers, Aryabhata carefully studied the works of his predecessors, borrowing and building on their ideas in his writings. Aryabhata was particularly interested in the work of the Greek arithmetician Diophantus on indeterminate equations and the ancient Hindu astronomer Parasara's studies of comets and planetary motion.

Life's Work

The culmination of Aryabhata's studies and struggles against myth was his masterwork, the *Aryabhathiya* (*The Aryabhatiya*, 1927), which he wrote, according to his own account, in 499. Three-quarters of *The Aryabhatiya* deals with astronomy and spherical trigonometry. The remainder is composed of thirty-three rules in arithmetic, algebra, and plane trigonometry, including quadratic equations, the sums of powers of the first *n* natural numbers, and a table of sines. This work represented what was then currently known, combined with his own theories.

Aryabhata's work in astronomy was very advanced for his time. He was the first Hindu known to have described Earth as a sphere, calculating the diameter at 1,050 *yojana*, or, at 7.6 miles per *yojana*, equal to 7,980 miles. This idea greatly troubled the Hindu priests, who stubbornly held to the traditional views of Earth presented in the Vedas and the Puranas. Earth, according to the Vedas, was flat and circular, with the heavens above, through which the moon, sun, and stars moved, with a middle air containing clouds, birds, and demigods between. The Puranas compared Earth's shape to that of the back of a turtle: round on the top and flat on the bottom, with the rounded part projecting above a surrounding body of water.

Aryabhata, with his naked eye, no doubt, carefully observed and diligently recorded the motion of the planets and stars, describing their orbits as circular or elliptical epicycles, noting the apsides and nodes. Predating Nicolaus Copernicus by a millennium, Aryabhata theorized that the apparent movement of these heavenly bodies was caused by the daily rotation of Earth about its axis and Earth's rotation around the sun. He understood how the tilt of Earth as it orbited the sun caused equinoxes and solstices.

Aryabhata explained that Earth was spun by a surrounding spherical sac of "aerial fluid" with a circumference of 25,790 miles. These were theories that would be greatly studied, and mostly rejected, by later Hindu astronomers, particularly Brahmagupta, who questioned the theory of an aerial fluid and wondered why lofty objects did not fall, if Aryabhata was indeed correct.

Aryabhata established a sect of astronomy that based its observations on the theory that the astronomical day began at sunrise at Lanka (Ceylon), through which passed both the Hindu meridian and the equator. Other sects established the beginning of the astronomical day at noon or midnight at Lanka and arrived at different results.

Although Aryabhata used mathematics as only a tool to understand astronomy, some of his mathematical theories are of interest and importance.

The first Hindu known to have studied algebra, Aryabhata gives the sum of the first, second, and third powers of the first n natural numbers, the solution integers of certain indeterminate equations of the first degree, and the general solution of a quadratic equation.

In *The Aryabhatiya*, Aryabhata presents a table of sines of angles for use in astronomy. In order to do so, Aryabhata had to make considerable advances over the trigonometry of Hipparchus and Ptolemy. These two scholars, for example, in studying an angle of 60° formed by two rays emanating from the center of a circle, had studied the chord and arc subtended by the angle. One of Aryabhata's major advances was to consider instead half of the length of the chord, associated with half of the angle, in this case 30°. Thus, he built the right triangle that forms the basis of all modern trigonometric functions. Aryabhata found that the half-chord (which he called by the Hindu word *jiva*) of 30° was 1710′. Aryabhata calculated a number of *jiva*, which are really sines, for different angles in the first quadrant, at intervals of 3.75°; his results appear in a table in *The Aryabhatiya*. To calculate his values, Aryabhata used a formula probably equivalent to:

$$\sin(n + 1)a - \sin na = \sin na - \sin(n - 1)a - \sin na/\sin a$$

a formula, correct except for the last term, which he may have taken from the *Surya Siddhanta* (400), an anonymous Hindu work on astronomy from the fifth century.

Aryabhata also presented ideas that contributed to the solving of indeterminate equations such as an equation presented by Diophantus, $ax \pm by = c$, where a, b, and c are constant integers. This work was later built on by Brahmagupta. Aryabhata also solved the divisor problem of $x = q_1t_1 = q_2t_2 + r_2$, using the continued fraction method. He was interested in the latter equation for its usefulness, among other things, in studying the Hindu calendar year, which he calculated to be equal to 365 days.

Aryabhata also put forth the basic but extremely useful tool of inversion. Stated simply, inversion meant finding the solution by converting addition to subtraction and multiplication to division, as extraction of the square root becomes squaring, and vice versa. In one famous problem he asks (in the typical style of the time) a beautiful maiden with "beaming eyes" to calculate according to the method of inversion the number which, when multiplied by 3, increased by ¾ of the product, divided by 7, diminished by ⅓ of the quotient, multiplied by itself, diminished by 52, then, following the extraction of its square root, increased by 8, and finally divided by 10, gives the number 2. The method of inversion calls for starting with the number 2 and working backward, inverting each operation, to reach the answer, 28.

Aryabhata also devised formulas for extracting square roots and cube roots. His formulas—$(a + b)^2 = a^2 + 2ab + b^2$ and $(a + b)^3 = a^3 + 3a^2b$

$+ 3ab^2 + b^3$—involved first dividing a number into periods of two and three digits, indicating that Aryabhata probably knew of the principle of number positions and may have known about zero. The ideas of number position and zero, perhaps for the first time in Hindu mathematics, were explicitly presented in the improved number system of Bhāskara I, one of the pupils whom Aryabhata taught following the completion of *The Aryabhatiya*. (Bhāskara I must be differentiated from later scholars of the same name.)

Aside from teaching, Aryabhata continued to write on mathematics after completing his masterwork, *The Aryabhatiya*. He completed a treatise in which he expounded the *arddharatrika* system, but the work has been lost. Around 530, Aryabhata calculated an extremely accurate value for π (62,832/20,000 or 3.1416), which he may have discovered through examination of a regular polygon of 384 sides. Although this approximation for π was more accurate than any figure previously given by the Babylonians, the Egyptians, or Archimedes (207-212 B.C.), neither Aryabhata nor any other Hindu mathematician before the twelfth century used it. They preferred to use the traditional but less accurate values of $^{22}/_{7}$, $\sqrt{10}$, $^{16}/_{9}$, or simply 3.

Summary

Aryabhata's work is an odd mixture of the correct and mistaken. He correctly calculated the formula for the area of an isosceles triangle, which is one half of the base multiplied by the height. Yet, he badly botched the formula for the volume of a sphere. His formula, $\pi^{3/2}r^3$, would make π equal to 16/9, or 1.78, a far less accurate figure than the 3.1416 which he had elsewhere calculated. This error was possibly derived from the $(^{16}/_{9})^2$ or 3.16 given by Ahmes (c. 1550 B.C.). Aryabhata also erred with the formula for the volume of a pyramid, stating that it was equal to half of the product of the base and the altitude.

Aryabhata correctly stated that the moon and the primary planets did not shine their own light but rather reflected that of the sun. He used this knowledge to determine what caused eclipses. He incorrectly thought, however, that the stars also reflected the light of the sun. He understood that Earth rotated, yet he believed that the stars, despite their complex orbits, were in fixed places in the heavens. Any unbiased consideration of the sum of his work must consider his mistakes along with his achievements.

Despite the importance of Aryabhata's achievements, his work did not readily reach the scientific center of Ujjain. When it finally did reach Ujjain, it greatly interested Brahmagupta, Bhaskara, and other scholars, who in particular studied Aryabhata's work on indeterminate equations and the structure of the solar system. One indication of the high regard in which *The Aryabhatiya* was held by the Hindus is that at least twelve commentators wrote on it. Aryabhata's work also reached the Arabs, and it was translated around 800 under the title *Zij al-Arjabhar*, Arjabhar being the Arabic translation of Aryabhata. This translation appeared two or three decades after Brahmagupta's masterwork, the *Brahma sphuṭa siddhānta* (c. 628), had been translated into Arabic. Together, these two books, by the first two great Hindu astronomer-mathematicians, greatly influenced the development of nascent Arabian mathematics.

Bibliography

Cajori, Florian. *A History of Mathematics*. London: Macmillan, 1919, 2d ed. 1924. A comprehensive history of mathematics, with a particular emphasis on the formulas used by various mathematicians. Cajori gives information on Aryabhata's work on inversion, extraction of square and cube roots, indeterminate equations, and π.

Dube, Bechan. *Geographical Concepts in Ancient India*. Varanasi, India: National Geographic Society of India, 1967. This work expounds ideas of Hindu scientists ranging from the layout of houses and the shape of Earth to the structure of the universe. It also includes information on Aryabhata's concept of the calendar.

Eves, Howard. *An Introduction to the History of Mathematics*. New York: Holt, Rinehart and Winston, 1964, 3d ed. 1969. Textbook that covers the history of mathematics up to the beginning of calculus. This book was one of the first to include mathematical problems at the end of each chapter. It includes information on Aryabhata's work on inversion, formulas for the volumes of spheres and pyramids, and several terms for half-chords.

Hooper, Alfred. *Makers of Mathematics*. New York: Random House, 1948. Explains Aryabhata's place in the history of the development of sines.

Menon, C. P. S. *Early Astronomy and Cosmology*. London: George Allen and Unwin, 1932. A good overview of Hindu, Chinese, and Babylonian astronomy, with data on Aryabhata's contribution to Meru cosmology.

Smith, David E. *History of Mathematics*. 2 vols. New York: Dover Publications, 1958. A well-documented textbook covering everything from prehistoric math to calculus, with particular attention to the geographic and racial considerations as well as a chronological sequence. Volume 1 presents a formula Aryabhata used for summing an arithmetic series after the *p*th term and some interesting information on Pataliputra. Volume 2 gives a portion of Aryabhata's table of sines, compared to modern values, and the formula he may have used to calculate them.

Waerden, B. L. van der. *Science Awakening*. Translated by Arnold Dresden with additions by the author. Groningen, Netherlands: P. Noordhoff, 1954. An unusually well-illustrated history of mathematics, the volume contains many useful diagrams and photographs of texts. It also includes an explanation of a system of numerical notation used by Aryabhata and some information on his pupil Bhāskara I.

Frank Wu

ASCLEPIADES OF BITHYNIA

Born: 124 B.C.; Prusa (Cios), Bithynia
Died: c. 44 B.C.; Rome
Area of Achievement: Medicine
Contribution: Asclepiades was the first physician to establish Greek medicine in Rome.

Early Life

Asclepiades, whose father was probably Andreas, a noted physiologist of the time, was born in Prusa, also called Cios, in Bithynia, Asia Minor. A widely read man, he seems to have had a liberal education in his youth. Apparently, there was enough money for him to be able to travel and study.

After studying rhetoric and medicine in Athens and Alexandria, he practiced medicine, first in Parion, a town on the Hellespont (Dardanelles), and later in Athens. After extensive traveling, in the year 91 he settled in Rome, where he may have become a Roman citizen. A man of amiable manners, good fortune, and worldly prosperity, Asclepiades formed friendships with such prominent individuals as Cicero and Marc Antony.

Preferring the freedom of a solitary life in a suburban villa, Asclepiades refused the invitation of King Mithradates of Pontus to join his court. Though he did not participate in public debates, he was not afraid to disagree with others. He condemned all those who thought that anatomy and physiology were the foundation of medicine. He was responsible for introducing Democritus' atomistic philosophy to Rome.

His daily routine included three basic activities: visiting and treating the sick throughout the city, giving written advice, and writing books. Although he was a voluminous author, little remains of the twenty or more treatises he prepared. Specific dates of his works are not known; the fragments that remain have been assigned English titles according to their subject matter. He wrote one book of definitions, one commentary on some of the short and obscure works of Hippocrates; one treatise on fevers, and three on febrile, inflammatory, and acute diseases. He also wrote *Concerning Common Aids*, a precursor of modern guides to healthy living; *Enemata*, which was frequently quoted by Aulus Cornelius Celsus in *De medicina* (c. A.D. 30; English translation, 1830); and *Method of Giving Wine in Sickness*.

Asclepiades also offered public lectures on medicine and had a large number of students. Applying many of his principles, these students, led by Themison of Laodicea, later founded the Methodist school, which emphasized diet and exercise in the treatment of illness.

By the age of thirty, Asclepiades was already famous. Some of that fame had grown from a story about him which circulated in Rome. According to this story, one day Asclepiades encountered a funeral procession. Just as the

Forestier sculp.

corpse was placed upon the pyre and the fire was about to be lit, he ordered the ceremony stopped, had the body taken down and delivered to his home, administered restoratives, and soon revived the man.

A statue excavated in Rome in 1700 was assumed to be a correct likeness of Asclepiades. From this it would appear that he was a man of slender stature who possessed a rather tranquil countenance.

Life's Work

Asclepiades was one of the foremost physicians of his century, exhibiting rich practical and philosophical attainments, versatility of mind, and an ability to make rapid diagnoses. Opposing the Hippocratic idea that morbid conditions resulted from a disturbance of the humors of the body, he held that nothing happened without a cause and that the causes of events were always mechanical—that is, dependent upon matter and motion.

The medical practice that Asclepiades founded was based on a modification of the atomic, or corpuscular, theory of Democritus, the Greek philosopher, according to which disease resulted from an irregular or inharmonious motion of the corpuscles of the body. Asclepiades believed that these masses were in continual motion, splitting into fragments of different shapes and sizes which then re-formed to create perceptible bodies. These particles were separated by invisible gaps, or pores. Friction between the particles created normal body heat; jamming the pores, or obstruction, was the cause of fever and inflammatory disorders. Fainting, lethargy, weakness, and similar complaints were attributed to an abnormal relaxation of the pores. Since disease was attributed to either constricted or relaxed conditions of the body's solid particles, Asclepiades founded his therapy on the efficacy of systematic interference as opposed to the healing power of nature. The regimens that he prescribed incorporated such therapies as fresh air, light, appropriate diet, hydrotherapy, massage, clysters or enemas, local applications, and, occasionally, very small amounts of medication.

For those complaints which he believed to be caused by obstruction, he proposed various kinds of exercise to relax the pores; in this way, the free transmission of the interrupted atoms or molecules would be facilitated. For pain, localized venesection might be cautiously practiced, but only for instant relief, because bleeding tended to draw off the finer, more vital atoms first and leave the coarser atoms behind. Rigor, or rigidity of the body, might result.

He believed that dropsy, an excessive accumulation of fluid in the tissues, resulted from an infinite number of small holes in the flesh that converted all the food received into water. How such a conversion might occur, however, he did not explain. To illustrate that the brain was the seat of the finest atoms, he performed decapitation experiments on animals such as eels, tortoises, and goats.

Asclepiades condemned purgatives, emetics, and drugs. Instead, he relied greatly on changes in diet, accompanied by friction, bathing, and exercise. He paid special attention to the patient's pulse. His remedies were directed to the restoration of harmony, based on the fundamental principle that treatments should be given promptly, safely, and pleasantly. For relaxants, he used wine and massage; to stimulate patients, he used wine, cold water, vinegar, and narcotics. He taught that patients tolerated diseases differently. Exercise, in his view, was unnecessary for healthy people. In cases of dropsy, he recommended making small cuts near the ankles to release the fluid. He advised that, when tapping was done to remove fluid, the opening be made as small as possible.

Asclepiades was particularly interested in psychiatric cases. He placed these patients in brightly lit, well-ventilated rooms, used occupational therapy, prescribed exercises for improving the memory and increasing attention, soothed them with music, and used wine to induce sleep.

According to Pliny the Elder, the Roman naturalist and writer, Asclepiades had three principal modes of cure. The early stages of illness often called for "gestation," which consisted of being transported in some way such as a boat or litter to exhaust the patient's strength and cause fever. Asclepiades also used suspended beds that could be rocked, as well as hanging baths and other forms of hydrotherapy. He firmly believed and taught that one fever was to be cured by another. The second mode was friction or massage. The third mode was wine, which he gave to febrile patients and used as a stimulant in cases of lethargy. He believed that it was necessary to force a patient to endure thirst. All patients were required to fast during the first three days of illness. In later stages, wine and moderate amounts of food were allowed.

Asclepiades showed great accuracy in distinguishing between various diseases, describing and dividing them into acute and chronic classes. For example, he gave a correct description of malaria; he also observed the psychic complications that occurred in cases of pneumonia and pleurisy. His special attention was devoted to chronic diseases, conditions which had been somewhat neglected by Hippocrates.

Asclepiades wagered that he would never die of disease; indeed, he is not known to have ever fallen ill. His death, at an advanced age, was the result of an accidental fall down a flight of stairs.

Summary

Asclepiades of Bithynia may be ranked as the first physician to introduce Greek medicine to Rome. A full assessment of his merits cannot be made because most of his writings have been lost. The fragments of them which have surfaced in later literature deal with subjects such as the pulse, respiration, heart disease, ulcers, climate, drugs, and the preparation of remedies.

By the fourth century, Asclepiades was almost forgotten. His critics had characterized him as a man of natural talents acquainted with human nature and possessed of considerable shrewdness but little scientific or professional skill. Galen strongly opposed him because Asclepiades had been the first to attack and repudiate the humoral teachings of Hippocrates. Pliny also disliked him and regarded him as a charlatan.

On the other hand, Celsus, the first compiler of medical history and procedures, admitted that he learned much from Asclepiades. Galen grudgingly credited Asclepiades as having pioneered two surgical procedures, laryngectomy and tracheotomy. As has been noted, his ideas were influential in the development of the Methodist school, with its emphasis on diet and exercise. Furthermore, Asclepiades was a pioneer in the humane treatment of mental patients.

Bibliography

Allbutt, Sir Thomas C. *Greek Medicine in Rome: The Fitzpatrick Lectures on the History of Medicine Delivered at the Royal College of Physicians of London in 1909-10*. London: Macmillan, 1921. This series of lectures addressed to interested physicians and others with a strong medical background may be too abstract for the general reader. It is a complete medical history of the period with extensive commentary on all major figures, but only one brief chapter on Asclepiades. Excellent illustrations, bibliography, and additional chronology.

Cumston, Charles Greene. *An Introduction to the History of Medicine: From the Time of the Pharaohs to the End of the Nineteenth Century*. New York: Alfred A. Knopf, 1926. This volume, which contains only one brief chapter on Asclepiades, is a compilation of numerous essential contributions to the general subject of a history of medicine. Written for the general reader and as an introduction for students of medicine, it is a lengthy work containing many illustrations but limited bibliographical material.

Gordon, Benjamin Lee. *Medicine Throughout Antiquity*. Philadelphia: F. A. Davis Co., 1949. Gordon's book contains only a very brief section on Asclepiades, along with scattered page references. The author makes mention of a wide-ranging array of facts that are not ordinarily accessible to a busy practitioner or to lay people interested in medical history. There are brief reference notes and a few illustrations but no chronology or bibliography.

Green, Robert M., ed. and trans. *Asclepiades, His Life and Writings: A Translation of Cocchi's "Life of Asclepiades" and Gumpert's "Fragments of Asclepiades."* New Haven, Conn.: Elizabeth Licht, 1955. Green has prepared a complete translation of *Discorso primo di Antonio Cocchi sopra Asclepiade* (c. 1740) and of selections from Christian Gumpert's *Fragmenta* (1794), a compilation of extant writings of Asclepiades. This volume contains the most detailed information available in English for the general reader, although it lacks reference notes and a bibliography.

Major, Ralph. "Medicine in the Roman Empire." In *A History of Medicine*. Springfield, Ill.: Charles C Thomas, 1954. This chapter includes a brief section on Asclepiades. There is no presumption of background knowledge about medical history. Very limited information is presented and few illustrations are given. There is no chronology and only a limited bibliography.

Rawson, Elizabeth. "The Life and Death of Asclepiades of Bithynia." *Classical Quarterly* 32, no. 2 (1982): 358-370. Rawson presents a critical analysis of the information known about Asclepiades. A scholarly approach utilizing much research in Latin and Greek sources, but no translations of the numerous quotes are given. It presumes extensive background knowledge concerning Asclepiades as well as the period in which he lived.

Rita E. Loos

JOHN JAMES AUDUBON

Born: April 26, 1785; Les Cayes, Haiti
Died: January 27, 1851; New York, New York
Areas of Achievement: Ornithology and art
Contribution: A gifted artist with a love of nature and a passion for discovery, Audubon became the greatest painter of birds of his time, an important natural scientist, and an inspiration to conservationists.

Early Life

John James Audubon, American naturalist, was born in Haiti on April 26, 1785, the illegitimate son of Jean Audubon, a French naval officer, and Jeanne Rabin, a French servant girl from Brittany. After his mother's death, Audubon's father took him and a younger half sister to France, where he legally adopted his children in 1794. In school, Audubon early revealed his talents for drawing and music. He learned to play the violin and flute and by age fifteen had begun drawing birds and collecting birds' eggs. After he proved unfit for a naval career, the elder Audubon sent him to Mill Grove, his farm near Valley Forge, Pennsylvania. In 1808, following a four-year engagement, Audubon married Lucy Bakewell, a girl of English descent who lived on a neighboring estate. Of their four children, two sons—Victor Gifford and John Woodhouse—survived to adulthood and provided significant help to their father in his painting and publishing projects.

In the United States, Audubon formed a partnership with Ferdinand Rozier, an older Frenchman whom his father had sent to look after him. They became frontier merchants, with stores in Kentucky, first in Louisville, then in Henderson, and finally in Ste. Genevieve, Missouri. Yet Audubon preferred to trek the forests, observing and painting birds and other wildlife. Finding business irksome, he dissolved the partnership and entered into an ill-fated trade arrangement with his brother-in-law, Thomas Bakewell. In 1813, Audubon and a group of associates built a combination sawmill and gristmill in Henderson, Kentucky. It proved far too ambitious a project to be sustained by the local economy, and its failure left him bankrupt. After being imprisoned for debt, he worked as a taxidermist for the Western Museum in Cincinnati, receiving additional income from portrait painting. In 1820, he set out for New Orleans to continue work as an artist, but, more important, to add to his portfolio of bird paintings. His wife worked as a tutor to support the family, and the two endured many months apart before she joined him in Louisiana.

Life's Work

For Audubon, an avocation developed into a vocation, though it is not known precisely when the change occurred. In 1810, while he and Rozier

Library of Congress

were in their Louisville store, Alexander Wilson, the pioneer American ornithologist, showed them his bird paintings and sought a subscription to support publication of his nine-volume *American Ornithology* (1808-1814). After seeing Wilson's work, Rozier remarked that his partner's paintings were better. By allowing Audubon to realize that his amateur work surpassed the work of a professional, this incident probably served as a catalyst to his fertile imagination.

He gradually developed the idea for *The Birds of America* (1827-1838), an ambitious portfolio of all American species, life-size, in their natural habitats. In its scope, scale, and fidelity to nature, Audubon's work would eclipse that of his predecessors. In order to include all the known species, he would rely upon the discoveries and observations of others for some of his paintings, not limiting the work to his own observations as Wilson had done. By the time he left for New Orleans in late 1820, the outlines of the work, which would require almost two decades to complete, were formed.

An experienced hunter and skilled woodsman, Audubon combined an intense interest in nature with a sharp eye and essential survival skills. He was equally comfortable alone or in company, and equally ingratiating to Indians or European noblemen. At five feet ten and a half inches tall, he was a man of almost regal appearance, with smooth facial lines, long brown hair, somewhat receding, and blue eyes. A contemporary, Mrs. Nathaniel Wells Pope, described him as "one of the handsomest men I ever saw . . . tall and slender. . . . His bearing was courteous and refined, simple and unassuming."

In Audubon's time, a naturalist needed to collect specimens (usually by shooting), to record his observations in a journal, and to sketch or paint all that he found interesting. To collect specimens, he shot thousands of birds on his expeditions. The collecting, however, did not stop there: He obtained insects, reptiles, and mammals for many other scientists throughout the world. In his lengthy journals, often romantic and even grandiloquent in tone, he made detailed notes about bird sightings and behavior. An almost compulsive painter, he sometimes began sketching a bird by placing its body on a sheet of paper and drawing an outline. Although Audubon occasionally painted live birds, his normal mode was to paint dead ones, which he wired into positions that suited him.

After his efforts to interest New York and Philadelphia publishers in his work failed, Audubon embarked in 1826 for England, where he attempted to attract wealthy patrons for his project by exhibiting his paintings. There, where he was regarded as a natural untaught genius, he became something of a celebrity, being named a fellow of the Royal Society. For *The Birds of America* he sought two hundred subscribers willing to pay one thousand dollars each; he eventually obtained 161, about half of them from the United States. Subscribers paid for a set of five prints at a time, with eighty sets, or four hundred prints, projected.

The publication, requiring eleven years, began in 1827, in Edinburgh, under the engraver William Lizars. Audubon quickly changed to Robert Havell and Company in London, after Havell impressed the painter with his ability to reproduce color tones. The images were etched on copper plates using aquatint, producing shades of gray and black on a light background. They were engraved on sheets measuring thirty-nine and a half by twenty-six and a half inches, forming the Double Elephant Folio, one of the largest books ever printed. After the engraving, artists colored the prints professionally by hand to match Audubon's original paintings.

When completed, the work included life-size color prints of 489 species on 435 pages. The total number of bird paintings was 1,065, for Audubon attempted to illustrate different color phases of each species, and for birds of varied coloration he often produced several poses to reveal the colors more effectively. One of his own favorite paintings, that of the wood duck, includes four birds so positioned as to reveal the rich coloration of the species. His painting of the little blue heron shows a full-size adult in the foreground and, at a distance, standing in a marsh, the white immature representative of the species.

During the production of his major work, Audubon returned to the United States three times to collect more specimens and to complete his paintings, leaving publication in the hands of his son Victor and Havell. In the United States, he mounted extended expeditions into the interior of the country, along the Gulf of Mexico, and to Labrador. Meanwhile, with the assistance of the gifted Scottish ornithologist William MacGillivray, he prepared and issued five volumes of commentaries as companion volumes to the paintings, *Ornithological Biography* (1831-1839). The work names and describes each species, provides an account of its behavior and habitats, and often includes vivid narration of Audubon's experience with the species, the primary source being his unpublished journals.

After completing *The Birds of America*, Audubon issued the work in a smaller and less expensive edition. He then turned to a new project, this time concerning North American mammals, *Viviparous Quadrupeds of North America* (1846-1854; plates, 1842-1845), in collaboration with his friend John Bachman. Seeking specimens to paint, he organized his last great expedition in 1843, traveling up the Missouri River to the mouth of the Yellowstone in North Dakota. After age sixty, he suffered a rapid decline in health, marked by a loss of mental powers. He died quietly at his New York home, Minnie's Land, on January 27, 1851, leaving completion of his work on the mammals to his sons and to Bachman.

Summary

In ornithology, art, and conservation, Audubon's fame and influence have endured. During his time, taxonomy was in its early stages, and science developed largely through observation and compilation. Vast areas of the world lay unexplored and unstudied. To discover new species of flora or fauna was an obvious route to achievement, possibly even to fame. Never a theorist and little inclined toward experimentation, Audubon possessed intense curiosity about nature, keen eyes, and a questing, somewhat romantic nature. He discovered a dozen subspecies, more than twenty species, and one genus of American birds. The list, though impressive, is shorter than he believed, because he mistook several variant color phases for new species and unwittingly claimed some prior discoveries of others.

The artistic quality of *The Birds of America* surpassed that of its predecessors, and the work has not been equaled since in its scale, scope, and aesthetic appeal. Although he occasionally painted with oils, Audubon achieved his best effects using watercolors with an overlay of pastels to enhance color and sharpen detail. Critics, however, have called attention to his limitations as an artist. He sometimes posed his subjects in unnatural positions and uncharacteristic settings, gave some birds human expressions, and could not sustain a uniformly high aesthetic level throughout the long project. Yet he succeeded in arousing widespread interest in ornithology and made the birds of the New World familiar to the Old.

In the twentieth century, his name has become synonymous with conservation of wildlife, a legacy not without irony considering the number of birds he felled with his gun. Still, toward the end of his life, he spoke out against egg collecting as a threat to bird populations. During his final Western expedition, he was troubled by the indiscriminate slaughter of bison. He genuinely loved the primitive frontier and feared that it might disappear under the pressure of civilization. In 1886, his protégé and admirer, George Bird Grinnell, organized the first Audubon Society to preserve some of the natural beauty and living creatures of the land Audubon loved.

Bibliography

Audubon, John J. *The 1826 Journal of John James Audubon*. Edited by Alice Ford. Norman: University of Oklahoma Press, 1967. Careful editing and extensive commentary supplement this important surviving Audubon journal. It reveals Audubon as a careful observer of birds from shipboard during his journey to England.

Chancellor, John. *Audubon: A Biography*. London: Weidenfeld and Nicholson, 1978. A readable brief biography of Audubon, with a judicious assessment of his achievement. Rich in illustrations.

Ford, Alice. *John James Audubon*. Norman: University of Oklahoma Press, 1964. Now the standard biography, it gives a carefully researched account of Audubon's origins and early life, adding extensive details about his early life in France.

Fries, Waldemar H. *The Double Elephant Folio: The Story of Audubon's*

Birds of America. Chicago: American Library Association, 1973. A scholarly historical and bibliographic account of the production and distribution of Audubon's greatest work. Traces the location and provides description of all extant copies.

Harwood, Michael. "Mr. Audubon's Last Hurrah." *Audubon* 87 (November, 1985): 80-117. A lengthy account of Audubon's journey to North Dakota in 1843, the article provides numerous excerpts from his journals and those of contemporaries.

Harwood, Michael, and Mary Durant. "In Search of the Real Mr. Audubon." *Audubon* 87 (May, 1985): 58-119. This article traces Audubon's career in detail, assesses the many myths that surround him, and provides a critique of his biographers. Generously and judiciously illustrated, with numerous reproductions.

Herrick, Francis Hobart. *Audubon the Naturalist: A History of His Life and Time*. 2 vols. New York: D. Appleton and Co., 1917, 1938. Although somewhat dated in its research, the biography remains a valuable resource for its comprehensive treatment and its inclusion of many original letters, papers, official records, and documents.

Lindsey, Alton A. *The Bicentennial of John James Audubon*. Bloomington: Indiana University Press, 1985. A collection of essays by various hands, the book assesses Audubon's character, his contributions to science and art, and his influence on conservation.

Stanley Archer

AVICENNA
Abu ‘Ali al-Husain ibn ‘Abd-Allah ibn Sina

Born: August or September, 980; Afshena, Transoxiana Province of Bukhara, Persian Empire
Died: 1037; Hamadhan, Iran
Areas of Achievement: Philosophy, medicine, law, astronomy, and philology
Contribution: Avicenna was the first Islamic thinker to synthesize the philosophy of Aristotle and Plato with Islamic traditions. His writings on medicine were studied in Europe as late as the seventeenth century.

Early Life

Abu ‘Ali al-Husain ibn ‘Abd-Allah ibn Sina was born in 980 to Abd-Allah of Balkh (now in Afghanistan), the well-to-do governor of an outlying province under Samanid ruler Nuh II ibn Mansur. Avicenna may have descended from a Turkish family on his father's side, but his mother, Sitara, was clearly Iranian.

After his brother, Mahmud, was born five years later, the family moved to Bukhara, one of the principal cities of Transoxiana and capital of the Samanid emirs from 819 to 1005. Exhibiting an early interest in learning, young Avicenna had read the entire Koran by age ten. His father was attracted to Isma‘ili Shi‘ite doctrines, preached locally by Egyptian missionaries, but Avicenna resisted his father's influence. There was much discussion in his home regarding geometry, philosophy, theology, and even accounting methods. Avicenna was sent to study with an Indian vegetable seller who was also a surveyor. It was from him that Avicenna became acquainted with the Indian system of calculation, making use of the zero in computations.

A well-known philosopher came to live with the family for a few years and had an extraordinary influence on the young scholar. Abu ‘Abd Allah al-Natili stimulated Avicenna's love of theoretical disputation, and the youth's earlier readings in jurisprudence enabled him to tax al-Natili's powers of logic daily. The tutor convinced Abd-Allah that Avicenna's career should be only in learning. Avicenna was studying Aristotelian logic and Euclidean geometry when the teacher decided to move to a different home. Soon Avicenna had mastered texts in natural sciences and metaphysics, then medicine, which he did not consider very difficult. He taught physicians, even practicing medicine for a short time. At the age of sixteen, he was also engaging in disputations on Muslim law.

For the next year and a half, Avicenna returned to the study of logic and all aspects of philosophy, keeping files of syllogisms and praying daily at the mosque for guidance in his work. So obsessed did he become with philosophical problems and so anxious to know all that he hardly took time for sleep. Aristotle's *Metaphysica* (*Metaphysics*) became an intellectual stum-

bling block until his reading of a work by Abu Nasr al-Farabi clarified many ideas for him. Soon all of Aristotle became understandable, and Avicenna gave alms to the poor in gratitude.

When Sultan Nuh ibn Mansur of Bukhara became ill, he sent for Avicenna, upon the advice of his team of physicians. Because of his help in curing the ruler, Avicenna gained access to the palace library, thus acquainting himself with many new books. When not studying, Avicenna was given to drinking wine and satisfying a large sexual appetite which he retained to the end of his life. Avicenna claimed that after the age of eighteen he learned nothing new, only gained greater wisdom. When the palace library was destroyed in a fire, critics blamed Avicenna, who, they said, wished to remove the sources of his ideas. There is no proof of that charge.

Life's Work

Avicenna's writing career began in earnest at the age of twenty-one with *al-Majmu* (1001; compilation), a comprehensive book on learning for Abu al-Hasan, a prosodist. Then he wrote *al-Hasil wa al-mahsul* (c. 1002; the sun and substance), a twenty-volume commentary on jurisprudence, the Koran, and asceticism. There soon followed a work on ethics called *al-Birr wa al-ithm* (c. 1002; good works and evil). The sponsors made no copies of them, a matter of some concern to the author.

His father died in 1002, and Avicenna was forced to take government service. He reluctantly left Bukhara for Gurganj, the capital of Khwarazm, where he met Emir Ali ibn Ma'mun. From Gurganj, he moved to Fasa, Baward, Tus, Samanqan, and thence to Jajarm on the extreme end of Khurasan. He served Emir Qabus ibn Wushmagir until a military coup forced Avicenna to leave for Dihistan, where he became ill. After recovering, he moved to Jurjan.

In Jurjan, Avicenna met his pupil and biographer, Abu 'Ubaid al-Juzjani, who stayed with him throughout much of the remainder of his life. Juzjani thought him exceptionally handsome and wrote that when Avicenna went to the mosque on Friday to pray, people would gather to observe at first hand "his perfection and beauty." While in Jurjan, Avicenna wrote *al-Mukhtasar al-awsat* (the middle summary on logic), *al-Mabda' wa al-ma'ad* (the origin and the return), and *al-Arsad al-kulliya* (comprehensive observations). There also Avicenna wrote the first part of *al-Qanun fi al-tibb* (*Canon of Medicine*), *Mukhtasar al-Majisti* (summary of the *Almagest*), and yet other treatises. One modern scholar lists one hundred books attributed to him. Another says that the list of Avicenna's works includes several hundred in Arabic and twenty-three in Persian.

From Jurjan, Avicenna next moved to al-Rayy, joining the service of al-Saiyyida and her son, Majd al-Dawlah. Civil strife forced him to flee to Qazwin; from there he moved to Hamadhan, where he managed the affairs of Kadhabanuyah. He was called to the court of Emir Shams al-Dawlah to treat the ruler for colic, after which Avicenna was made the vizier of his emirate. Because of a mutiny in the army, however, the emir was forced to discharge him. After matters calmed down, Avicenna was called back and reinstated as vizier. During this period, public affairs occupied his daytime hours, and he spent evenings teaching and writing. When the emir died, Avicenna went into hiding, finishing work on his *Kitab al-shifa* (book of healing). He was arrested for corresponding with a rival ruler, but when Emir 'Ala' al-Dawlah attacked Hamadhan four months later, Avicenna was set free.

Avicenna left Hamadhan for Isfahan with his brother, two slaves, and al-Juzjani to serve Emir 'Ala' al-Dawlah. The emir designated every Friday evening for learned discussions with many other masters. Not present was a famous scholar and rival of Avicenna, Abu al-Rayhan al-Biruni, with whom he carried on a rather bitter correspondence. They had been clients at many of the same courts, but never at the same time. At Isfahan, Avicenna completed many of his writings on arithmetic and music. He was made an official member of the court and accompanied the emir on a military expedition to Hamadhan.

When he was rebuked by the emir's cousin, Abu Mansur, for feigning expertise in philology, Avicenna was so stung by the criticism that he studied this subject frantically, compiling his discoveries in a book entitled *Lisan al-'Arab* (the Arabic language). During these years, he also continued other experiments in medicine and astronomy. He introduced the use of medicinal herbs and devised an instrument to repair injured vertebrae. He understood that some illnesses arose from psychosomatic causes, and he wrote extensively on the pulse, preventive medicine, and the effects of climate on health. On May 24, 1032, he observed the rare phenomenon of Venus passing through the solar disk.

When he became ill in Isfahan, one of his slaves filled his meal with opium, hoping for his death and an opportunity to steal his money. Yet Avicenna managed to recover under self-treatment. Soon, however, he had a relapse; he died in 1037. Most authorities say that he died and was buried in Hamadhan.

Summary

The *Canon of Medicine* remained a principal source for medical research for six centuries, perhaps second only to the Christian Bible in the number of copies produced. Between 1470 and 1500, it went through thirty editions in Latin and one in Hebrew; a celebrated edition was published on a Gutenberg press in Rome in 1593. Avicenna's principal literary contribution was the invention of the Rubaiyat form, quatrains in iambic pentameter, later made famous by Omar Khayyam. Most important of all, Avicenna's philosophical system helped to stimulate a genuine intellectual renaissance in Islam that had enormous influence not only in his own culture but in Western Europe as well. Thomas Aquinas, Averroës, John Duns Scotus, Albertus Magnus, and Roger Bacon learned much from Avicenna, even though they disagreed on some particulars.

Most intriguing to the medieval Scholastics were Avicenna's insistence upon essences in everything, the distinction between essence and existence (a notion derived from al-Farabi), the absence of essence in God (whose existence is unique), and the immortality of the soul (which animates the body but is independent of it).

According to some scholars, Avicenna's insistence upon observation and experimentation helped to turn Western thought in the direction of the modern scientific revolution. His theories on the sources of infectious diseases, his explanation of sight, his invention of longitude, and his other scientific conclusions have a truly remarkable congruence with modern explanations. The application of geometrical forms in Islamic art, his use of the astrolabe in astronomical experiments, and his disputations on the immortality of the soul demonstrate Avicenna's universal genius.

Bibliography

Afnan, Soheil M. *Avicenna: His Life and Works*. London: George Allen and Unwin, 1958. The author stresses the impact of Avicenna's philosophy upon the thinkers of the Arabic-speaking world.

Arberry, Arthur J. *Avicenna on Theology*. London: John Murray, 1951. This important brief work contains Avicenna's own autobiography and its continuation by his disciple and companion, Abu 'Ubaid al-Juzjani, as well as Arberry's discussion of Avicenna's defense of monotheism and the immortality of the soul.

Avicenna. *The Life of Ibn Sina: A Critical Edition*. Translated by William E. Gohlman. Albany: State University of New York Press, 1974. Contains an annotated edition of Avicenna's autobiography, the contemporary account of his life by Juzjani, and a critical examination of the bibliography about Avicenna.

Brown, H. V. B. "Avicenna and the Christian Philosophers in Baghdad." In *Islamic Philosophy and the Classical Tradition: Essays to Richard Walzer*, edited by S. M. Stern, Albert Hourani, and Vivian Brown. Columbia: University of South Carolina Press, 1973. A clear presentation of Avicenna's philosophical differences with both Aristotle and the Peripatetic thinkers of the Baghdad school, despite his fundamental adherence to the rationalism of Aristotelian traditions. The Greek master's ambivalence on the purposiveness of nature led Avicenna to reject any rational choice in nature, in contrast to the approach of the Baghdad scholars.

Copleston, Frederick. *A History of Philosophy*. Vol. 2. Westminster, Md.:

Newman Press, 1955. Copleston clarifies not only the contributions of Arab philosophy to European medieval thought but also the diversity within this Islamic renaissance. Particular attention is focused upon Avicenna and Averroës.

Goichon, Amélie M. *The Philosophy of Avicenna and Its Influence on Medieval Europe*. Translated by M. S. Khan. Delhi: Motil al Banarsidass, 1969. Three lectures, originally in French, make up the three chapters of this fine work on the main theses of Avicenna's philosophy, the adaptation of the Arabic language to Hellenic thought, and the influence of Avicenna's ideas on European intellectual developments in the Middle Ages. Not addressed are Avicenna's contributions to medicine and the natural sciences.

Hitti, Phillip K. *Makers of Arab History*. New York: St. Martin's Press, 1968. This eminent historian of the Arab world discusses Avicenna and twelve other outstanding figures, from Muhammad to Ibn Khaldun. A valuable feature of this work is its incorporation of eight historical maps.

Maurer, Armand A. *Medieval Philosophy*. New York: Random House, 1962. Reprint. Toronto: Pontifical Institute of Mediaeval Studies, 1982. Maurer presents a summary of Avicenna's arguments on being, necessity, and essence; on proofs for the existence of God; on the doctrine of creation; and on man's intuitive knowledge of his soul. Although an Aristotelian, Avicenna, according to Maurer, also had links with the Neoplatonists and the later followers of Saint Augustine.

Morain, Lloyd L. "Avicenna: Asian Humanist Forerunner." *The Humanist* 41 (March/April, 1981): 27-34. A valuable article containing numerous reproductions of artifacts and sketches of Avicenna. Anatomical drawings used in Avicenna's writings and other depictions of his medical treatments appear in this article as well as portraits, a commemorative stamp, and a photograph of his mausoleum.

Peters, F. E. *Aristotle and the Arabs*. New York: New York University Press, 1968. *Falsafah*, the term used to describe the tenth century reception of classical Greek science and philosophy, was in fact a blend of Hellenic learning with Islamic ideas. This is the subject of Peters' book, but the synthesis of which he writes is not only that of Islam and Hellenism but that of scholarship on this subject since the nineteenth century.

John D. Windhausen

CHARLES BABBAGE

Born: December 26, 1791; in or near London, England
Died: October 18, 1871; London, England
Areas of Achievement: Mathematics, invention, and computer science
Contribution: Babbage conceptually anticipated many of the developments realized in twentieth century computation science. He contributed to the mathematics of his time and invented several practical devices.

Early Life

Charles Babbage, the first child of Benjamin and Elizabeth (Teape) Babbage, was born on December 26, 1791. The exact location of his birth is not known, but it was in the vicinity of London, where his father was a well-to-do banker. The family, on both sides, had been comfortably established in the nearby countryside for several generations. Two more sons were born but died in early childhood. A daughter, Mary Anne, outlived her brother Charles, with whom she had a lifelong close relationship.

As a young child, Charles was subject to fevers, which were naturally of great concern to his parents; when it came time for some formal education, he was placed under the tutelage of a clergyman with the admonition "to attend to his health, but not to press too much knowledge upon him." He later attended school in Enfield, where he was instructed in the classics. Charles's natural aptitude for mathematics in particular, and logical, systematic thinking in general, manifested itself early. As a schoolboy he discovered algebra and, for several months, arose at 3 A.M. for self-instruction along with a similarly precocious classmate.

As he grew older, Charles became more robust, and as an adult he was full-figured and rather handsome. When he was twelve years old his parents moved back to Totnes, where they had lived before going to London. That was Charles's home until he entered Cambridge University in 1810.

By that time his mathematical self-instruction had progressed into differential and integral calculus. He was very disappointed to find himself far in advance of the mathematical instruction available at the university.

At Cambridge his social nature developed. He had many friends and joined in numerous nonacademic activities. In addition, Babbage's liberal political consciousness emerged, curiously manifesting itself, in part, by his espousal of Gottfried Wilhelm Leibnitz's calculus notation over that of England's Isaac Newton. With a group of like-minded fellow undergraduates, he formed the Analytical Society to study the mathematical developments being made on the Continent.

He was graduated from Cambridge University in 1814. Soon thereafter, against his father's wishes, he was married to Georgiana Whitmore. The young newlyweds settled in London, but Charles continued his studies,

receiving his M.A. degree in 1817. He had no income-producing position at that time, but family moneys allowed the couple to live quite comfortably in London society. Charles was accepted in scientific circles and was elected to the Royal Society in 1816.

Life's Work

The only professional appointment that Babbage ever held was to the Lucasian Chair of Mathematics at Cambridge University (1828-1839), an appointment that had few formal duties. Consequently, and by virtue of his private wealth, he was free to pursue his own interests from his home in London.

For a dozen years after he and Georgiana settled there, he thoroughly enjoyed the social and intellectual atmosphere of the city. Eight children were born to them. Only four survived infancy, and Georgiana died in childbirth with the eighth in 1827. Babbage, devastated by the loss, became an increasingly bitter and sharply critical man. He spent the year following his wife's death traveling on the Continent. He never remarried or had a normal home life again. His surviving children were reared by relatives living outside London. Of the four, the only daughter, also named Georgiana, died as a young girl. Only after they had reached adulthood did Babbage get to know his sons well.

Nevertheless, Babbage, a gregarious man of great vitality, traveled widely and associated with a broad circle of contemporaries such as Charles Darwin and Charles Dickens as well as with fellow scientists at home and abroad. He was a great admirer of the scientific developments in Germany and France and of their associated educational institutions and professional societies. He was a significant force in establishing in England the Cambridge Philosophical Society, the Astronomical Society, the Statistical Society of London, and the British Association for the Advancement of Science. In 1830, he wrote *Reflections on the Decline of Science in England and on Some of Its Causes*, deploring the sad state of the Royal Society in England at the time.

Babbage continued to pursue his mathematical interests beyond his university days, publishing a number of significant papers in the areas of the calculus of functions, algebraic analysis, probability, and geometry. Since this was at a time when British mathematics had reached a dismally low level, Babbage's mathematical work was held in especially high regard on the Continent.

One of the important mathematical needs of that time was for tables of trigonometric, logarithmic, and other functions. Those in existence had been laboriously generated by human calculators and were not without error. About 1821, Babbage, impressed by the potential of machines to carry out fixed operations and recognizing that successive entries in such tables could be expressed in terms of finite differences, conceived of an infallible calculating machine to replace fallible human calculators. The calculated results would be automatically printed out to eliminate transcribing errors.

In constructing his first mechanical calculator, the "Difference Engine," Babbage was assisted by sizable funding from the British government, which recognized the importance of accurate tables for use in navigation, for example. He designed the engine and personally supervised its construction by a skilled, hired engineer. In connection with this activity Babbage devised some new machine tooling techniques and an unambiguous method of Mechanical Notation for parts drawings to aid in communication between designer and engineer. A working model was built which may be seen in the British Museum of South Kensington.

The upset associated with his wife's death interrupted further developments for the machine planned by Babbage. After his return to England he faced difficulties with his engineer and with obtaining further government funding. No more work was done on the Difference Engine after 1832. By that time, however, Babbage had conceived of a much more sophisticated and versatile "Analytical Engine," one which embodied many ideas now familiar in the world of electronic computers.

The Analytical Engine had a storage unit for holding numerical input data, a mill for working on them, and a separate operations control section, and he used punched-card systems for input and operation. The rest of Babbage's life—and much of his private fortune—was devoted to improving and refining these basic ideas. Only a modified version of the Analytical Engine was ever built but detailed plans for several versions of it were carefully drawn up which show the soundness of Babbage's ideas.

In England, Babbage was widely regarded as an eccentric, irascible genius, but he was much respected abroad. In 1840, he traveled to Italy, where he gave a series of lectures on his Analytical Engine that was especially well received. A member of the audience, L. F. Menabrea, wrote up those lectures and published them in French. Subsequently, they were translated into English and provided with a lengthy commentary by Countess Ada Lovelace, the daughter of the poet Lord Byron. She was a mathematically precocious teenager when she first met Charles Babbage in 1833. He was pleased with her interest in and appreciation of his calculating machines, and the warm friendship which developed between them lasted throughout her sadly short lifetime.

Babbage was a prolific writer on social, political, economic, religious, as well as technical topics. He was the outstanding cryptologist of his time, using mathematical techniques to decipher the codes devised by others. In addition, he invented many practical devices, such as an occulting light which could be used to send messages and an opthalmoscope for studying the eye. The American scientist Joseph Henry, who visited Babbage on two occasions, wrote of him:

> Hundreds of mechanical appliances in the factories and workshops of Europe and America, scores of ingenious expedients in mining and architecture, the construction of bridges and boring of tunnels, and a world of tools by which labor benefited and the arts improved—all the overflowings of a mind so rich that its very waste became valuable—came from Charles Babbage. He more, perhaps, than any man who ever lived, narrowed the chasm separating science and practical mechanics.

Summary

Charles Babbage enjoys higher and more widespread esteem today than he ever did during his lifetime. Many of his ideas regarding computing machines have been realized only in the late twentieth century, with the advent of modern electronic devices. In his time he was the leading advocate of the systematic application of science to industry and commerce and of statistical methods to economic and social problems—what would today be called "operations research."

Babbage was a man born ahead of his time. Disappointed with the current state of affairs in England, unappreciated, even snubbed at times in his home country, he nevertheless looked forward with optimism to the future which could be made by the application of scientific principles. He has been quoted as saying that he would willingly give up the rest of his life to be able to return five hundred years hence with a guide to explain the intervening advances that he believed were sure to come.

Bibliography

Babbage, Charles. *Passages from the Life of a Philosopher*. London: Longman, Green, Longman, Roberts and Green, 1864. Thirty-six autobiographical fragments of very uneven quality and style.

Babbage, Henry P., ed. *Babbage's Calculating Engines, a Collection of Papers Relating to Them: Their History, and Construction*. Los Angeles: Tomash Publishers, 1982. Facsimile reprint of 1889 edition published by E. and F. N. Spon and Co. of London, recently made available as volume 2 of the Reprint Series for the History of Computing under the auspices of the Charles Babbage Institute at the University of Minnesota. Includes a new introduction by Allan G. Bromley. Contains thirty-three items, most of them assembled by Charles Babbage before his death. Additions and editing provided by his youngest son.

Dubbey, J. M. *The Mathematical Work of Charles Babbage*. Cambridge: Cambridge University Press, 1978. A critique of the mathematical work of Babbage with extended commentary on the calculus of functions, mathematical notation, and the mathematical basis of the operation of his calculating engines. Includes a list of all of Babbage's mathematical books and papers.

Goldstine, Herman H. *The Computer from Pascal to Von Neumann*. Princeton, N.J.: Princeton University Press, 1972. Chapter 2, "Charles Babbage and His Analytical Engine," describes the concepts developed by Babbage that are inherent in modern computing. Shows how Babbage built upon what previously had been accomplished by others and introduced significant conceptual advances.

Hyman, Anthony. *Charles Babbage: Pioneer of the Modern Computer*. Princeton, N.J.: Princeton University Press, 1982. Full-length biography based on the author's extended research on published works and archival materials. Analyzes the social and political climate of Babbage's time and his involvement aside from his technical achievement. Lists all Babbage's published works. Mathematical discussion of Babbage's engines placed at end of text as appendices.

Merz, John Theodore. *A History of European Scientific Thought in the Nineteenth Century*. 2 vols. New York: Dover Publications, 1965. Republication of a work originally published between 1904 and 1912. Chapters 1-3 of volume 1 compare and contrast the scientific spirit in France, Germany, and England during the lifetime of Charles Babbage; includes several references to Babbage.

Morrison, Philip, and Emily Morrison, eds. *Charles Babbage on the Principles and Development of the Calculator*. New York: Dover Publications, 1961. Selections from the Babbage volumes listed above with an insightful introduction by the editors summarizing the life and works of Babbage.

Moseley, Maboth. *Irascible Genius: A Life of Charles Babbage, Inventor*. London: Hutchinson and Co., Publishers, 1964. Focuses on personal details of Babbage's life. Quotes extensively from correspondence deposited in archives.

Stein, Dorothy. *Ada: A Life and a Legacy*. Cambridge, Mass.: MIT Press, 1985. Biography of Augusta Ada Byron, later Countess of Lovelace, with extensive discussion of her relationship with Charles Babbage.

Katherine R. Sopka

FRANCIS BACON

Born: January 22, 1561; London, England
Died: April 9, 1626; London, England
Areas of Achievement: Philosophy, science, and politics
Contribution: The first to use English instead of Latin for a philosophical treatise with his *The Twoo Bookes of Francis Bacon of the Proficience and Advancement of Learning Divine and Humane*, Bacon is credited with the formulation of modern scientific thought. His *Essayes* is widely admired for its worldly witticism and has become a classic of the form.

Early Life

Francis Bacon was born January 22, 1561, at York House in London, to Sir Nicholas Bacon, Lord Keeper of the Seal of England, and his second wife, née Ann Cooke, who was related to nobility through her sister, the wife of Sir William Cecil, the later Lord Treasurer Burghley. In 1573, at the age of twelve, Bacon entered Trinity College, Cambridge, which he left in 1576 for Gray's Inn, thus following in his father's steps and beginning a legal career.

After a brief visit to the French court in the entourage of Sir Amias Paulet from 1576 until his father's death in 1579, Francis Bacon stayed with the Inn and was called to the bar in 1582, two years before he began to complement his legal work with an ambitiously undertaken political career that commenced with his membership in Parliament.

After advancement to the position of Queen's Counsel in 1589, his career stalled under Elizabeth I, whom he seemed to have offended in a parliamentary debate regarding the implementation of regal subsidiaries in 1593; his enemies at court used the opportunity to bar his way to promotion, seeing in Bacon (not wholly unjustly) not only an ambitious, prolific writer of political advice but also an unscrupulous seeker of preferment. Again, on the personal level, his friendship with the young Earl of Essex did not bring him hoped-for political gain; in 1601, after Essex's ill-considered rebellion against the queen, Bacon's position required him to partake in the prosecution of his former friend.

Whereas *An Advertisement Touching the Controversies of the Church of England* (1589) had brought Bacon political advancement, his later work of political advice did not professionally benefit him. During a long period of arrested political development until Elizabeth I's death, Bacon showed himself stubborn and inclined to use the common practice of patronage and favoritism to lobby for a higher position. In his own office, he became a rather successful mediator of conflicts and tried hard but finally inefficiently to smooth the waves after Essex's insubordination preceding his open revolt against the queen.

A later painting shows Bacon as a tall, bearded officer wearing his regalia

Library of Congress

and insignia proudly; the picture suggests the reserved, somewhat unemotional yet nevertheless personally sensitive character which his later biographers have asserted on the basis of accounts from Bacon's chaplain and secretary William Rawley. At forty-five, he married Alice Barnham, daughter of a London alderman, who survived him; they had no children.

Life's Work

His long period of relative political inactivity under Elizabeth I gave Bacon time to write the first ten of his *Essayes*, which saw publication in 1597, and again, because of their popularity, in 1612 and in 1625, both times with significant enlargements which brought the total number to fifty-eight. A master of the essay form, which he helped to forge, Bacon here looks at men and their government realistically, free of passionate idealism and zeal for the betterment of man. What his critics have called his "Machiavellian" and "emotionless" coldness nevertheless facilitated a witty discourse on the world as it really is, and not as it should be in the eyes of reformers. With this was coupled political advice, as in "On Dissimulation" or "On Plantations," against the shortsightedness, greed, and abuses of his time.

The Twoo Bookes of Francis Bacon of the Proficience and Advancement of Learning Divine and Humane (1605) which he later enlarged into the Latin version *De Augmentis Scientiarum* (1623), represents his first step toward the formulation of a new method for looking at the natural world through the eyes of the experimenting and hypothesizing scientist who has purged his vision of religious allegory or Platonic metaphysics or Aristotelian dialectics.

Bacon's political fortunes changed in the reign of James I, which saw his ascension from his knighthood in 1603 through the office of attorney general (1613) to the high position of Lord Keeper in 1617, before he was made Lord Chancellor and Baron Verulam and ultimately created Viscount St. Albans in 1621, at the age of sixty.

During these years of success, Bacon wrote the *Magna Instauratio* (1620, "great instauration"), the planned preface, never completed, for six different works intended to describe a restoration of human knowledge; as is, it is a powerful model for radical change in the pattern of Western scientific thought, characterized by Bacon's clear sense of ordering and classification. *Novum Organum*, published in the same year, contains Bacon's argument for a "new logic," the discovery of a finite number of "natures" or "forms" lying at the base of the natural world, and an exhaustive description of natural history.

After he had reached the zenith of his power, Bacon's fall came when old enemies charged him with bribery; he admitted to the charges since he had indeed not only taken gifts from suitors, which was more generally acceptable, but also had accepted donations from individuals whose cases were pending with him as their judge (and in which he often decided against them despite the offerings given). Bacon resigned from his office, was fined forty thousand pounds, was briefly imprisoned in the Tower of London, and was banished from the court. He made slow progress at rehabilitation, but at the time of his death in the house of Sir Arundel in 1626, he had not yet received full royal pardon from the new king Charles II.

Summary

Although his public fall from grace as a result of misconduct in office linked Francis Bacon to his literary model Seneca, who showed similar excellence in thought and corruption in public life, the British naturalist and statesman must be remembered for his new, practical approach toward the natural environment; his proposed outlook at science bears the seeds of modern scientific thought.

In his last, unfinished work, *New Atlantis*, posthumously published in 1627, Bacon argues that there is no conflict between the free pursuit of scientific exploration and the dogmas of the Christian religion. He sums up the ancient Hebrew view of the natural world as there to use and explore rather than as the manifestation of sundry natural deities, and he connects this thought to the idea that scientific research is ultimately undertaken so that God (the final spiritual authority) "might have the more glory" in the "workmanship" of the scientists and men "the more fruit" in the "use" of their discoveries.

On a final note, Bacon's idea, in the utopian *New Atlantis*, for an organization dedicated to the free pursuit of all natural sciences which would collect and display its findings in central "houses," has been realized in the British Royal Society and the British Museum, two institutions which, founded in the spirit of Bacon, are thriving today.

Bibliography

Anderson, Fulton H. *Francis Bacon: His Career and His Thought*. Los Angeles: University of Southern California Press, 1962. Based on a series of lectures, this work attempts to link Bacon's philosophy with his politics and to relate his thought to contemporary problems.

__________. *The Philosophy of Francis Bacon*. Chicago: University of Chicago Press, 1948, 1971. Influential book revealing Bacon's thoughts primarily through his own words. Somewhat dry and overinclusive, it makes up for the lack of critical discussion with its useful compilation of primary texts.

Bacon, Francis. *The Works, the Letters, and the Life of Francis Bacon*. Edited by James Spedding, R.L. Ellis, and D.D. Heath, 14 vols. London: Longmans, 1857-1874. Includes William Rawley's *The Life of the Right Honourable Francis Bacon* (1657). Still the authoritative, standard edition of Bacon's complete work. Detailed biography with an impressive collection of primary sources such as Bacon's letters and notes. The standard against which all later works have to be judged.

Bowen, Catherine Drinker. *Francis Bacon: The Temper of a Man*. Boston: Little, Brown and Co., 1963. Enjoyable biography which brings Bacon alive while not neglecting scholarly accuracy. Careful and perceptive; Bowen's favorable portrait forgives Bacon almost everything but his coldness toward women.

Bozeman, Theodore Dwight. *Protestants in an Age of Science: The Baconian Ideal and Antebellum American Religious Thought*. Chapel Hill: University of North Carolina Press, 1977. Traces the roots of modern fundamentalism to the antebellum Presbyterians, who used Bacon's idea to prove themselves right and all their pre-Darwinian opponents wrong. An interesting contribution to the history of ideas.

Church, R. W. *Bacon*. London, 1881. A nineteenth century biography which has stayed amazingly fresh over the years. Church's readable, precise style provides an enjoyable encounter with Bacon, whose personality is emphasized.

Eiseley, Loren. *Francis Bacon and the Modern Dilemma*. Lincoln: University of Nebraska Press, 1963. Slim booklet emphasizing Bacon's achievements as a scientist; does not account for his deficient understanding of mathematics. Eiseley stresses Bacon's view of an integrated, responsible science.

Farrington, Benjamin. *The Philosophy of Francis Bacon*. Liverpool: Liverpool University Press, 1964. Valuable discussion of Bacon's philosophical ideas; Farrington includes a fine translation of Bacon's minor Latin works and thus makes them accessible to a broader audience.

Fuller, Jean Overton. *Sir Francis Bacon*. London: East-West Press, 1981. Ingeniously relates events in Bacon's life to contemporaneous passages from Shakespeare's work. Lavishly produced reiteration of the generally discredited theory that Bacon was the true author of Shakespeare's oeuvre.

Rossi, Paolo. *Francis Bacon: From Magic to Science*. Translated by Sacha Rabinovitch. Chicago: University of Chicago Press, 1968. Examines the European magical and alchemical tradition of science which Bacon rejected. Important bibliography.

Reinhart Lutz

ROGER BACON

Born: c. 1213; Ilchester, Somerset, England
Died: c. 1292; probably Oxford, England
Areas of Achievement: Science, education, and philosophy
Contribution: Bacon was a pioneer in the development of the scientific experimental method, and he advocated educational reform based on secular, scientific disciplines.

Early Life

Roger Bacon was born into a family of minor nobility sometime during the year 1213 in Ilchester, Somerset, England. Although very little is known concerning his life prior to 1239, he was trained in his youth in the classics and in the quadrivium (arithmetic, geometry, astronomy, and music). He studied the liberal arts at Oxford University and received his baccalaureate from either Oxford or the University of Paris around 1239. Soon thereafter, he received a master of arts from Paris and began his teaching career there as a regent master on the arts faculty.

During Bacon's early professional years, he lectured on Aristotelian and pseudo-Aristotelian treatises—especially the *Secretum secretorum* (fourth century B.C.), a long letter of advice on kingship and practical affairs supposedly written by Aristotle to Alexander the Great—but he exhibited no indication of his later preoccupation with science. As an eclectic thinker during this period from 1239 to 1247, Bacon blended his Aristotelian ideas with certain Neoplatonist elements derived from many different sources. Nevertheless, he was one of the first Parisian masters to lecture on the forbidden books of Aristotle soon after the Church lifted the ban. There, he wrote his early scholastic works and commentaries on grammar, dialectics, physics, metaphysics, and astronomy. He also popularized the ideas of Avicenna, al-Ghazali, and Averroes, thus integrating Arabic thought with that of the West. Again, his eclecticism led him to criticize the Moslem savants on many issues, especially when they espoused concepts that he considered to be anti-Christian or antiscriptural.

About 1247, a major change occurred in Bacon's intellectual development. Abandoning his teaching position in Paris to return to Oxford, he devoted all of his time, and large sums of money raised mainly from family members, to experimental research, to acquiring certain "secret" books, to constructing scientific instruments and tables, to training assistants, and to conferring with scholars of like mind. These activities marked a definite departure from the usual routine practiced by his colleagues. Through these endeavors he became immensely impressed with the benefits that science could bestow upon religion—a "universal" science that would include all the secrets of nature.

Library of Congress

This change probably was caused by the Oxford environment and the influence exerted there by Robert Grosseteste (whom Bacon may never have met personally), a leader in introducing Greek learning to the West and an early advocate of the experimental method. Bacon was also impressed by Adam Marsh, Grosseteste's most famous associate, and by Thomas Wallensis, the bishop of St. David's.

From 1247 to 1257, Bacon devoted himself to the study of languages, optics, alchemy, astronomy, and mathematics. He campaigned against hearsay evidence, denounced rational, Platonist deductions, and extolled experimentation so relentlessly that he began to anger the more traditional scholars. Although his role as an experimenter may be exaggerated historically and his originality may not have produced significant scientific or technological breakthroughs, he did operate a quasi-laboratory for alchemical experiments and did carry out systematic observations with lenses and mirrors. Also important was his work on the nature of light (reflection, refraction, and spherical aberration) and on the rainbow. Of lesser significance were his ideas on flight, gunpowder, mechanically propelled land vehicles and seacraft, and eclipses of the sun.

Life's Work

About 1252, Bacon joined the Franciscan Order (soon after Grosseteste had bequeathed his library to them), but from the beginning he appears to have been unhappy. He had difficulty acquiring scientific equipment, he abhorred his colleagues' disinterest in his work, and he resented the preference shown by his superiors to the more orthodox teachers on the faculty. Within several years, he became embittered and began to level criticisms (often unjust) at some of the best minds of his age. Yet for a time, he was permitted to engage in scientific speculation and observation without interference.

In 1257, he was transferred to the Frairs Minor convent at Paris, possibly because of the aforementioned personal difficulties but certainly not for his scientific endeavors. His feverish activity, amazing credulity, supposed superstition, and vocal contempt for those who opposed him obviously irritated the established English members. He would always feel suspicion, and his increasing physical infirmities and lack of support would plague him for the remainder of his life.

From 1257 to 1266, Bacon taught mathematics, perspective, and philosophy at the Franciscan *studium*. Eventually, the Order's hostility to his ideas forced him to appeal to Pope Clement IV (Cardinal Guy de Foulques), whom he may have known when the latter was in the service of the Capetian kings. In correspondence of 1266, the Pope referred to letters that he received from Bacon that described various aspects of the natural world, mathematics, languages, physics, and astrology. Bacon envisioned the production of an encyclopedia—a massive compendium of all verifiable knowledge—to be put to the ultimate service of theology. He stated that such a scientific work would be of great value in confirming Christian faith, in maintaining the welfare of the Church and the universities, and in sponsoring educational reform. Desiring a fuller understanding of this project, the Pope ordered Bacon to send him detailed information and to proceed in total secrecy because of the Franciscan rule against unauthorized writing.

In obedience to the Pope's command, Bacon set to work in 1266 and in a remarkably short period of approximately eighteen months produced the *Opus majus* (1267), the *Opus minus* (1267), and the *Opus tertium* (1267-1268). The *Opus majus* contains all of his basic ideas for educational reform based upon the supremacy of the sciences. The second and third works were largely synopses. The death of the Pope in November of 1268 dealt a crushing blow to Bacon's chances of an official reception and extinguished his lifelong dream. The Pope may not have read any of them.

Bacon divided the *Opus majus* into eight sections. The first delineated four barriers to truth: submission to untrustworthy authority, influence of custom, popular prejudice, and concealment of ignorance within philosophical jargon. The second showed the close relationship between philosophy and theology since they were both revealed by God to man. In section 3, Bacon stressed that all true scholars must be proficient in Hebrew, Greek, and Arabic if they desired to do meaningful research. Section 4 was a defense of the intimate correlation of the sciences with theology. Section 5 contained his theories of vision and optical science. In the sixth section—the most important—Bacon formulated his notion of experimental science. To him, experimentation certified the conclusions of deductive or mathematical reasoning, added new information to existing knowledge, and served to increase technological proficiency in both war and peace. The last two sections dealt with philosophical and political science questions that would be examined in greater depth by another Parisian master in the early years of the next century—Marsiglius of Padua in his *Defensor pacis* (1324).

Soon after the completion of these masterpieces, Bacon returned to England. He did little significant writing thereafter, save for some nonscientific works on grammar and philosophy. In 1272, he issued a highly polemical pamphlet directed against his opponents, and this produced more trouble for him within his order. A later source (the *Chronicle of the Twenty-four Generals* of 1370) reveals that he was imprisoned sometime between 1277 and 1279 for "suspected novelties" by the general of his order, Jerome of Ascoli (later Pope Nicholas IV). It is difficult, however, to determine what these "novelties" were since his ideas did not differ greatly from those of his contemporaries except in overall emphasis. The imprisonment, if indeed it were a true incarceration, was undoubtedly for personal reasons rather than for his scientific work. In any case, he was freed shortly before his death.

Summary

Roger Bacon was instrumental in laying the early foundation of modern scientific thinking. He was keenly aware of the interrelatedness of all the separate sciences and of the contributions that science makes to the understanding of reality. He explained the role of the experimental method in confirming or refuting speculative hypotheses. He insisted on the practical value of scientific speculation and believed in the importance of an ethical superstructure that would act as a system of checks and balances upon the discovery of new knowledge.

During his many years of scientific research, Bacon endeavored to discover all that could be known, but it seems clear that although he did some experimental work himself, his real claim to fame rests on his achievements as a scientific thinker and synthesist of other scholars' work. He has been credited, sometimes erroneously, with the introduction of gunpowder, eyeglasses, the telescope, and other technological developments. His works certainly describe these things and he understood the principles upon which they were based, but he never claimed credit for their invention. His experimental method may not be compatible with modern scientific method, but given the limitations of his time, his formulation was valid. In his conception of the immediate practical use of science, he was a harbinger of later work that led to the age of science in the early modern world. Roger Bacon did not create modern science; he inspired it.

Bibliography

Crombie, A. C. *Medieval and Early Modern Science.* 2 vols. Garden City, N.Y.: Doubleday Anchor Books, 1959. Extensive bibliographic coverage with detailed analyses of Bacon's contributions to calendar reform, scientific classifications, education, geography, geology, ophthalmology, optics, and physics.

____________. *Robert Grosseteste and the Origins of Experimental Science, 1100-1700.* Oxford: Clarendon Press, 1953. A detailed examination of experimentation in the thirteenth century and its relationship to modern scientific method.

Easton, Stewart C. *Roger Bacon and His Search for a Universal Science.* New York: Columbia University Press, 1952. Besides being an excellent bibliography of primary and secondary sources, Easton's account is valuable for its emphasis on Bacon's early life, educational experiences, Paris professorship, scientific contributions, religious conflicts, and impact on science and education.

Leff, Gordon. *Paris and Oxford Universities in the Thirteenth and Fourteenth Centuries.* New York: John Wiley and Sons, 1968. Bacon is cast within an institutional context that emphasizes university regulations, curricular requirements, teaching privileges, and intellectual developments. Special emphasis is placed on Aristotelianism and its influence on later medieval education.

Steele, R. "Roger Bacon and the State of Science in the Thirteenth Century." In *Studies in the History and Method of Science,* edited by Charles Singer. Oxford: Clarendon Press, 1921. The best early attempt to show the continuity of Bacon's scientific thought.

Thorndike, Lynn. *A History of Magic and Experimental Science.* 6 vols. New York: Macmillan, 1923-1941. Volume 2 contains many valuable discussions of Bacon's contributions to science; especially important for information on thirteenth century scientists and for criticism of those historians who overestimated Bacon's uniqueness. One of the seminal studies on this subject, based upon earlier Baconian publications by Thorndike in the *Philosophical Review* of 1914 and the *American Historical Review* of 1916.

Westacott, E. *Roger Bacon in Life and Legend.* New York: Philosophical Library, 1953. Among the more important topics covered are Bacon's principal works (in synopses, notably the *Opus majus*), his role as a medieval philosopher and scientist, and his creativity in the secular disciplines.

Ronald Edward Zupko

KARL ERNST VON BAER

Born: February 29, 1792; Piep, near Jerwen, Estonia
Died: November 28, 1876; Dorpat, Estonia
Areas of Achievement: Biology, anthropology, and geology
Contribution: Baer gained his greatest fame early in his career through his discovery of the mammalian egg and his contributions to the understanding of embryological development. In his later years, Baer would turn his attention to anthropological investigations, including the state of primitiveness of various races, and to geological studies, especially in Russia.

Early Life

In the mid-sixteenth century, an ancestor of Karl Ernst von Baer emigrated from Prussia to Livonia, and one of that ancestor's descendants bought an estate in Estonia during the mid-seventeenth century. He was made a member of the Prussian nobility, and by the time of Karl's father, Magnus Johann von Baer, the estate at Piep was of modest size. Karl's father was trained in law and served as a public official. Karl's parents were first cousins, and they had seven daughters and three sons. Because of the large size of the family, Karl was sent to live with his father's childless brother and wife on a nearby estate. It was there that Karl began to cultivate his love of botany and natural history.

He entered medical school at the University of Dorpat in 1810 but apparently never planned on a medical career. Instead, upon graduation, he continued his studies in Berlin, Vienna, and finally Würzburg. There he studied under the anatomist Ignaz Döllinger, a disciple of the German Romantic Friedrich Schelling, and was inspired to devote himself to the study of comparative embryology. In 1819, Baer finally received an appointment as an anatomy professor at Königsberg, where he stayed until 1834. That allowed him to marry Auguste von Medem, a resident of Königsberg, on January 1, 1820. They had five sons, of whom one died in childhood and a second of typhus at the age of twenty-one, and one daughter.

During Baer's tenure at Königsberg, he established himself as a brilliant embryologist and made his initial discoveries of the mammalian egg. His initial contributions are found in the first two volumes of Karl Friedrich Burdach's *Die Physiologie als Erfahrungswissenschaft* (1826-1828; physiology as empirical science). A small brochure entitled *De ovi mammalium et hominis genesis epistola* (1827; *The Discovery of the Mammalian Egg*, 1956) appeared at about the same time. In 1834, he left Königsberg for the Academy of Sciences in St. Petersburg, and in 1837 the still-unfinished second volume of his animal embryology was published, with the two volumes now entitled *Über Entwickelungsgeschichte der Thiere* (1828-1837; on

National Library of Medicine

the developmental history of animals). A portion of the missing material for this volume was published posthumously in 1888.

Life's Work

While at the University of Würzburg, Baer was encouraged by Döllinger and Christian Heinrich Pander to continue the largely unknown work of Caspar Friedrich Wolff concerning the detailed development of the hen's egg. Baer expanded that research to include a wide range of organisms, and the results of his studies virtually assured the epigeneticists of victory in their battle with the preformationists. He was the first to discover and describe the mammalian egg (first found in Burdach's house dog), and he concluded that "every animal which springs from the coition of male and female is developed from an ovum, and none from a simple formative liquid." This important theoretical statement, although based on German *Naturphilosophie* and rejected by later embryologists in the vitalistic terms understood by Baer, allowed for reproductive and embryological studies to continue on a doctrinally unified basis and hence permitted the development of comparative embryology as a discipline.

In addition to describing mammalian and other vertebrate ova, Baer described the developing embryo. One of his major conceptual innovations was that he could see the individual organism as a historical entity which underwent a developmental process. He thus examined organisms at various stages of development, and he was one of the first to describe the process in terms of the formation of germ layers and the gradual production of organs and body parts. Conducting research for the second volume of his monumental work, he examined and compared the developmental processes of different organisms. In the process, he discovered the notochord (the flexible supportive rod ventral to the nerve chord, which is characteristic of all chordates) in the chicken embryo, explained the significance of the gill slits and gill arches, which Martin Rathke had earlier discovered in the embryo, and then explained the cause of the amnion formation. Finally, he described the development of the urogenital system, the formation of the lungs, the development of the digestive canal, and the formation of the nervous system. These findings are detailed and commented on in his pioneering *Über Entwickelungsgeschichte der Thiere*.

Baer is best known for his remarks in the fifth scholium of this work, in which he argued against a single *scala naturae* (chain of being), presented a parody of Jean-Baptiste de Monet, chevalier de Lamarck, rejected evolution in any form as well as the idea that embryos of higher animals pass through the adult forms of the lower animals, and proposed his own laws of individual development. His comparative embryology had led him to the same conclusions that Georges Cuvier's comparative anatomy had produced, that is, that instead of a single chain of being, there were essentially four animal types. He further argued that comparative embryology actually provided better data than did comparative anatomy for classifying animals. Baer's method for classifying organisms was based on the fact that all animal embryos begin as a single fertilized egg. According to Baer, they diverged immediately into one of four types of development. Vertebrate embryos can be distinguished from the annulate embryos (essentially worms), which in turn are different from the embryos of the mollusks, and all of which differ from the radiata (echinoderms).

In addition, Baer argued that the more general traits of the group of animals to which an embryo belongs appear earlier in individual development than the specialized characteristics, that the more general form always precedes a more specialized form, that every embryo of a given form, rather than passing through the stages of other forms, instead diverges more and more from them, and that, as a result, the embryo of a higher form never resembles the adult of lower animals but only the embryonic form of those animals. He concluded that development takes place from homogeneous and general to heterogeneous and special and that ontological development reflects divergence from other forms rather than parallelism or recapitulation. With this latter conclusion, he thus argued against Johann Meckel's law of parallel development and against Ernst Haeckel's biogenetic law of ontogeny recapitulating phylogeny.

With the publication of the second volume of *Über Entwickelungsgeschichte der Thiere* in 1837, Baer had transformed embryology into a modern laboratory science. Moreover, he had produced a theoretical framework that would greatly influence evolutionary thought even though he would strongly maintain a lifelong antievolutionary position. Charles Darwin, for example, used embryological evidence to support his theory and noted that he agreed with Baer's view of divergence rather than the competing doctrine of recapitulation. Darwin also used Baer's standard for judging an organism to be "higher" than another as being related to the degree of differentiation of parts and specialization of function.

By the time the second volume of his great embryological work was published, Baer had left Königsberg for reasons that are not well understood and had settled in St. Petersburg, working at the Academy of Sciences. In 1846, he took a position with the academy in comparative anatomy and physiology, a decision that was related to his long-term interest in anthropology. Under the academy's auspices, he made a number of expeditions to such places as Novaya Zemlya, Lapland, the North Cape, and other regions of Russia as well as England and continental Europe. He collected specimens and made a number of geological discoveries. Although none of his work in these areas was as significant as his embryological achievements, he was instrumental in the founding of the Society of Geography and Ethnology of St. Petersburg and became a cofounder of the German Anthropological Society.

Baer retired from the academy in St. Petersburg in 1862 because of increasing problems with his vision and hearing. In 1867, he went to Dorpat, where he continued his studies and writing until 1876, when he died at the age of eighty-four.

Summary

Karl Ernst von Baer's contributions to the fledgling science of embryology in the nineteenth century were immeasurable. Methodologically and conceptually he provided the basis for further research. Yet apart from his empirical findings, little remains in modern biology of Baer's embryology. His adherence to German Idealism and *Naturphilosophie*, including the use of vitalistic explanations in embryological development, and his fervent anti-evolutionary position caused many scientists in the latter part of the century to ignore him. Nevertheless, his contributions were viewed as monumental during his time. He published more than three hundred papers on topics ranging from embryology and entomology to anthropology, Russian fisheries, and the routes of Odysseus' voyage. He was honored and respected by scientists throughout the world, and admired and loved for his loyalty and wit by his Estonian neighbors.

Bibliography

Baer, Karl Ernst von. *Autobiography of Karl Ernst von Baer.* Edited by Jane Oppenheimer. Translated by H. Schneider. Canton, Mass.: Science History, 1986. This relatively long autobiography was first published by the Estonian Knights in 1864 on the golden jubilee of Baer's doctorate. Oppenheimer provides a very helpful preface. An extensive bibliography and an index make this work a valuable tool for the serious student.

Coleman, William. *Biology in the Nineteenth Century: Problems of Form, Function, and Transformation*. New York: Cambridge University Press, 1977. Chapter 3 provides an excellent context for Baer's embryological work as it details the advances in cytology, explains the arguments between preformationists and epigeneticists, and describes the contributions that Baer made to the understanding of ontogeny.

Lovejoy, Arthur O. "Recent Criticism of the Darwinian Theory of Recapitulation: Its Grounds and Its Initiator." In *Forerunners of Darwin, 1745-1859*, edited by Bentley Glass et al. Baltimore: Johns Hopkins University Press, 1968. Lovejoy tries to explain why so many misread Baer. Explains Baer's four embryological laws, including what is and what is not affirmed. Examines Darwin's misreading of Baer and Baer's fallacies in his criticism of Darwin's theory. The notes provide helpful explanations.

Oppenheimer, Jane. "An Embryological Enigma in the *Origin of Species*." In *Forerunners of Darwin, 1745-1859*, edited by Bentley Glass et al.

Baltimore: Johns Hopkins University Press, 1968. Oppenheimer explores the professional relationship between Darwin and Baer. She examines the various ideas that each developed independently of the other and the diverse ways in which each incorporated these ideas into a total system. As a result, one understands how Darwin can use many of Baer's findings while rejecting his conclusion, and why Baer is unable to support Darwin's evolutionary position.

Ospovat, Dov. "The Influence of Karl Ernst von Baer's Embryology, 1828-1859." *Journal of the History of Biology* 9 (Spring, 1976): 1-28. This article discusses the degree of influence that Baer's embryological explanations had during his own life, especially in terms of their ability to dislodge the earlier theory of recapitulation. In the process, it clarifies the content of Baer's theories and shows the similarities to other theories then available as well as describes the essential points of difference between them. Ospovat also explains why he disagrees with some of the Baerean scholarship, including the articles by Oppenheimer and Lovejoy cited above.

Winsor, Mary P. *Starfish, Jellyfish, and the Order of Life: Issues in Nineteenth Century Science*. New Haven, Conn.: Yale University Press, 1976. While this book is not specifically about Baer, it is concerned with the issues and debates which surrounded his work and the work of other embryologists, comparative anatomists, taxonomists, and proponents of evolution. For that reason, it provides the scientific and philosophical context for understanding Baer.

Sara Joan Miles

SIR JOSEPH BANKS

Born: February 13, 1743; London, England
Died: June 19, 1820; Spring Grove, Heston Parish, Isleworth, England
Areas of Achievement: Exploration and natural science
Contribution: Combining his knowledge of botany and an inherited fortune, Banks led the scientific group on Cook's expedition in the *Endeavour* and, for forty-one years, as president of the Royal Society, supported and encouraged various scientific activities.

Early Life

Joseph Banks was born February 13, 1743, on Argyle Street, Westminster, London. He was the only son of William Banks, of Revesby Abbey near Lincoln, and his wife, the daughter of William Bate of Derbyshire, who is referred to as Sarah, Sophia, or Marianne by various writers. The Banks family was landed gentry, represented in Parliament and associated with all the great families in England. Mrs. Banks was strongly religious, but Joseph did not seem to follow any formal religion. He had a private tutor for some time; then, in April, 1752, he was sent to Harrow, and in September, 1756, to Eton. He was cheerful, with a generous disposition, but no student. At fourteen, he discovered the beauty of flowers and plants, embarking on a lifetime study. He was entered a gentleman commoner at Christ Church, Oxford, in December, 1760.

His father died in 1761, and Mrs. Banks moved to Turret House, Paradise Walk, Chelsea, with her daughter, Sarah Sophia. This was near the Chelsea Physic Garden. In Chelsea, Banks could pursue his botany and natural history interests while vacationing from Oxford.

Oxford's botany professor gave Banks permission to go to Cambridge to find a teacher. There, he met Israel Lyons, who was proficient in botany and mathematics. Lyons became a reader or lecturer in botany at Oxford, giving his series of lectures in July, 1764, paid for by pupil subscriptions organized by Banks. Banks's regular residence at Oxford ended in December, 1763, with irregular attendance in 1764 and 1765. In February, 1764, he had taken control of his inheritance, making him a wealthy young man. He made good progress under Lyons' teaching and attracted attention for his knowledge of natural history. In May, 1766, when he was elected a Fellow of the Royal Society at age twenty-three, Banks had already left on his first scientific exploration.

He joined an Oxford friend, Lieutenant Constantine Phipps, serving on HMS *Niger* on April 7, 1766. She was being sent to Labrador and Newfoundland on fishery protection duty under Sir Thomas Adams. Banks was her naturalist, and the two made observations and collections in Newfoundland, Labrador, and Portugal. Banks's journal was not published for almost two

Library of Congress

hundred years, nor was any formal report made to the Royal Society, where he attended his first meeting on February 15, 1767. His dried specimens became the basis for his herbarium, a center for the study of natural history. In 1767 and 1768, he toured parts of England and Wales, but nothing was published until 1899.

Banks abandoned his plans to visit Carolus Linnaeus in Sweden and Lapland in the spring of 1768 in order to concentrate on a Pacific expedition to observe the transit of Venus in 1769. The Admiralty agreed to fit out vessels and appointed Lieutenant James Cook commander of the *Endeavour* on May 25, 1768. Banks applied to the Council of the Royal Society to join in with ten others and, with the support of Lord Sandwich, the Admiralty gave approval on July 22, 1768.

The group included Dr. Daniel Carl Solander, a Swede and pupil of Linnaeus, who arrived in England in July, 1760, making an impact on English science and natural history. In 1764, he finally obtained an assistantship in the British Museum and was elected to the Royal Society. Banks met him in 1767. The principal artist was Sydney Parkinson, along with John Reynolds, Alexander Buchan, and Henry Spöring. Banks expended about ten thousand pounds of his own money outfitting himself and his staff. This was to be the first British voyage of discovery equipped with a scientific staff which was officially recognized.

The *Endeavour* sailed from Plymouth on August 25, 1768. Banks and Cook began journals, which complement each other, as did the men themselves. They sailed around the globe in three years, returning July 12, 1771. Banks examined the specimens collected, Solander described them, and Parkinson drew them. In Tahiti, Banks studied the natives and showed his ability to deal with people by getting back a stolen astronomical quadrant, which was needed to observe the transit of Venus. He lost his two black servants, Richmond and Dollin, who died at Tierra del Fuego. Buchan, the landscape artist, died at Tahiti, while the other three artists died before returning to England. Hundreds of new species were collected, new peoples and new lands were discovered, charting was done, and dangers overcome. Solander continued to work with Banks as associate and secretary until he died. Cook and Banks were hailed as heroes. Oxford granted Banks an honorary D.C.L. degree on November 21, 1771. A tradition of scientific work on British voyages of discovery had begun.

The travelers were summoned to Windsor to be received by George III, and Banks began a friendship which lasted his lifetime. Banks, Solander, and Cook also visited with Lord Sandwich in order to report on the voyage. John Hawkesworth, official recorder of this Cook voyage, worked with various journals, including Banks's, preparing three volumes, published in 1773. This, however, represented only a small part of the information gathered by the expedition.

Preparations were begun for a second voyage by Cook in the *Resolution*. Banks and Solander planned to take part, but with a larger group of assistants; as a result, extra quarters had to be constructed on deck. This made the ship too cumbersome, however, and Cook was concerned. Lord Sandwich and the Admiralty objected, and Banks withdrew. The scientists who finally sailed with Cook, in 1772, were Dr. Johann Reinhold Forster and his son Georg.

Banks then decided to go to Iceland. He chartered the brig, *Sir Lawrence*, for five months. Collections were made in Iceland with stops at the Orkney Islands and Scotland. The printed material and manuscripts formed the British Museum's Icelandic Collection. Descriptions of the natural pillars of Staffa and some drawings were published in *Tour in Scotland* by Thomas Pennant in 1774, but Solander's work on the flora of Iceland and most of the drawings were never published.

Life's Work

Banks took an active role working on the natural history collections of Cook's second and final voyages. He then took on the role of adviser and promoter of science for the rest of his life when George III selected Banks as his unofficial scientific adviser. Banks began to work on an open-air herbarium for exotic plants from all over the world at Kew Gardens. This encouraged botanical exploration, the study of economic uses of various plants, and the development of botanical gardens in other British settlements, the first in Jamaica around 1775.

Banks first served on the Council of the Royal Society in 1774, and, in 1778, was elected president. He also became an ex officio trustee of the British Museum, and he held both posts for more than forty years. This placed him in the forefront of all scientific activity. His London center was 32 Soho Square, the home of his growing library and botanical collections. His sister, Sarah Sophia, presided over the house. When he married Dorothea Hugessen, daughter of William Weston Hugessen of Norton of Kent, on March 23, 1779, Sarah continued to live with them. He also bought Spring Grove, in Heston, developing the gardens there with the help of his wife and sister. In 1781, he was made a baronet.

Solander's death in 1782 deprived Banks of an excellent secretary and associate and prevented the publication of Solander's manuscript. Many species in Australia and New Zealand had to be rediscovered later. Dr. Jonas Dryander, another Swede, became Banks's librarian and curator. Late in the summer of 1783, Banks had a carriage accident, after which he developed gout, which troubled him for the rest of his life.

Early in 1784, there was renewed interest in settlement in Australia, an idea presented by Banks in 1779. By 1786, he advised establishing a colony at New South Wales and continued to be active in the affairs of the new colony in Australia. He had many other interests: transplanting breadfruit from the Pacific to the West Indies for food; improving English wool quality by importing the first merino sheep from Spain; founding the African Society, which became the Royal Geographic Society; advising the East India Company on transplanting tea from China to India; supporting James Edward Smith in forming the Linnaean Society of London; getting Francis Bauer appointed at Kew Gardens in 1790; and selecting Archibald Menzies as naturalist for the Vancouver Expedition to the Northwest Pacific Coast, from 1791 to 1795.

Banks was invested with the Order of the Bath on July 1, 1795, taking the lizard as his device. He was sworn into the Privy Council in 1797. France honored him in 1802 with membership in the National Institute of France. When the Royal Horticultural Society was formed in 1804, Banks was present and became a vice president. He was also a member of the Society of Arts, the Engineers' Society, the Dilettanti Society, and the Society for the Improvement of Naval Architecture. He was active on the Council of the Society of Antiquaries, the Board of Longitude, and the Royal Institute.

In 1810, Robert Brown published his work on the plant collection from the Flinders Expedition and became Banks's secretary when Dryander died. Banks continued his vast correspondence, even during war times. In fact, he was responsible for saving the collections and helping foreign scientists on no fewer than ten occasions. He attended meetings and club dinners, even though he had to be carried or wheeled in a chair by his servants during the last fifteen years of his life. He continued to be active mentally, attending his last meeting in March, 1820. He died June 19, 1820, at Spring Grove and was buried in Heston Church with simple services and no headstone.

His will provided that Robert Brown was to have the use of his library and herbarium, and at Brown's death they were to go to the British Museum. Brown turned over the library and collections in 1827 and became keeper at the British Museum. The later scattering of Banks's papers and manuscripts through sales at Sotheby's has hindered efforts to produce a full biography, although his library and collections are still available and used in the British Library.

Summary

Sir Joseph Banks took an outstanding part in the celebrated first voyage of Cook (1768-1771). Along with his activities in Labrador and Newfoundland, Banks had established a pattern of collection and scientific exploration which enriched the British Museum and the rest of the world. He made his collections available to all, but it was unfortunate that he did not publish so that more people might have had easier access to his work. In his role as president of the Royal Society he supported individuals and a variety of scientific activities. In both botany and settlement support he is truly the "father of

Australia," and the first European to lead botanical investigation of New Zealand. He made the Royal Kew Gardens a world-renowned institution and helped develop numerous other botanical gardens throughout the world. He was a friend to king and commoner, a prodigious correspondent, a promoter of scientific societies and organizations in a wide range of fields, a promoter of scientific exploration, and an important link between the amateur tradition in British science and the modern scientific community.

Bibliography

Banks, Joseph. *The Endeavour Journal of Joseph Banks, 1768-1771*. Edited by J.C. Beaglehole. 2 vols. Sydney: Angus and Robertson, 1962. A carefully researched and faithfully presented version of Banks's journal and a fitting companion to Beaglehole's work on Cook. Here is the tale of the scattering of Banks's work around the globe. Beaglehole suggests that Banks did not publish because he was an amateur who lost interest in the work when completed.

———. *Journal of the Right Hon. Sir Joseph Banks, Bart., K.B., P.R.S. During Captain Cook's First Voyage in H.M.S. Endeavour in 1768-71 to Terra del Fuego, Tahite, New Zealand, Australia, the Dutch East Indies, etc.* Edited by Sir Joseph D. Hooker. New York: Macmillan, 1896. A one-volume version of Banks's journal, very much abridged. Contains information on the people mentioned in the journal and a biographical sketch of Banks, which Beaglehole considers full of errors. He mentions as sources Charles Richard Weld, *History of the Royal Society*; Sir John Barrow, *Sketches of the Royal Society and the Royal Club*; and B. Daydon Jackson, "Sir Joseph Banks," in *Dictionary of National Biography*.

Cameron, Hector Charles. *Sir Joseph Banks, K.B., P.R.S.: The Autocrat of the Philosophers*. London: Batchworth Press, 1952. A very readable account of Banks's wide range of activities, giving details on various individuals who were mentioned in the text. There are sections on Kew Gardens, Banks's correspondents, his role as president of the Royal Society, the founding of Australia, his promotion of science, his life at home, his detractors, and interesting appendices and illustrations.

Captain Cook's Florilegium. London: Lion and Unicorn Press, 1973. Thirty engravings from the drawings of plants collected by Joseph Banks and Daniel Solander on Captain Cook's first voyage to the islands of the Pacific, with accounts of the voyage by Wilfrid Blunt and of the botanical explorations and prints by William T. Stearn. Exquisite engravings based on the drawings and sketches of Sydney Parkinson with Solander's descriptions and collection data, and new names given by other botanists. There is also *Banks' Florilegium* (1979-). 750 engravings completed in 1784 at Banks's expense.

Cuvier, M. le B^r G. "Éloge Historique de M. Banks." In *Mémoires du*

Muséum d'Histoire Naturelle, vol. 13, 297-326. Paris, 1825. The transcript of a flowery eulogy given at a public meeting of the Royal Academy of Science on April 2, 1821 by M. Cuvier, perpetual secretary of the Academy. Cuvier gives Banks substantial credit for intervening on behalf of foreign scientists during wartimes. He also gives details of Banks's life and his various activities.

Lysaght, Averil M., comp. *Joseph Banks in Newfoundland and Labrador, 1766: His Diary, Manuscripts, and Collections*. London: Faber and Faber, 1971. A definitive presentation of Banks's journal and papers of his trip to Newfoundland and Labrador, 1766. Contains biographical sketches of key individuals, eighteenth century background, and the abilities of Banks at twenty-three. His biographical sketch includes his love affairs. There are excellent illustrations, and the book is well documented, with a fine index.

Maiden, J. H. *Sir Joseph Banks: The "Father of Australia."* London: Kegan Paul, Trench, Trübner and Co., 1909. Contains a brief personal sketch and comments on Banks, using long quotes from journals, letters, and other sources. It especially focuses on aspects of Australia. There are also brief sketches of men who worked with Banks, numerous illustrations, charts, works written, edited by, or concerning Banks, and a good index.

Oliver, W. R. B. "Botanical Discovery in New Zealand." In *Science* V (March, 1951): 17-48. Short account of Banks and his work in New Zealand, placing him in the context of the explorations from Europe which opened up the Pacific. Good portraits of leading botanists and eighteen illustrations of New Zealand plants and seeds. Asserts that if Solander's work had been published, his names would be on more than 340 native plants, instead of the names given by later botanists.

Smith, Edward. *The Life of Sir Joseph Banks, President of the Royal Society, with Some Notices of His Friends and Contemporaries*. London: John Lane, 1911. Started as a detailed life of Banks, but forced into abbreviation by the publisher, this work is a reference for most later comments on Banks. It contains seventeen illustrations, while the bulk of the work covers the period of Banks's life from his election as president of the Royal Society.

Mary-Emily Miller

BENJAMIN BANNEKER

Born: November 9, 1731; Baltimore County, Maryland
Died: October 9, 1806; Baltimore, Maryland
Areas of Achievement: Mathematics and astronomy
Contribution: Banneker's calculations provided the essential data for almanacs published from 1792 through 1797. A free black in a slave state, Banneker overcame obstacles of rural isolation, little formal education, racial prejudice, and alcoholism to establish himself as a respected scientist, earn a place on the crew that surveyed the District of Columbia, and become a symbol of racial equality in the abolitionist movement.

Early Life

Benjamin Banneker's American antecedents came in bonds to colonial Maryland. His grandmother, Molly Welsh, was a convict transported from England to Maryland in about 1683. After completing a period of servitude, she became a free landowner in the western part of Baltimore County near the Patapsco River. In 1692, Molly bought two Africans and in a few years restored freedom to both. One of the men, named Bannka, claimed to be the kidnaped son of an African king. In defiance of laws that forbade miscegenation, Molly married the prince and took Banneky as her surname.

The Bannekys had four daughters. The oldest, Mary, born in about 1700, married an African who recently had been given freedom as a baptismal gift. He had chosen Robert as his Christian name and, when married, took Banneky as his surname. The name's spelling varied until the mid-eighteenth century, when it settled at Banneker. Three of the four children born to Robert and Mary grew to maturity. The oldest, and the only son, was Benjamin, born on November 9, 1731.

In about 1729, Robert bought twenty-five acres of land close to Molly's farm. On March 10, 1737, when Benjamin was five years old, Robert purchased one hundred acres from the nearby Stout plantation. The title was in Robert and Benjamin's names to assure that the family could protect its freedom should Robert die suddenly. Maryland laws were not sympathetic to free blacks and authorized reenslavement of those who did not own property.

Banneker's education was rudimentary. His grandmother taught him to read from the Bible. For a few months, he attended a country school where the schoolteacher—probably a Quaker—taught black and white children. Benjamin learned to write a very clear, even beautiful, script and mastered the fundamentals of mathematics through basic algebra. At some point, he also learned to play the flute and the violin.

Though meager, this education powerfully shaped the course of Banneker's life. He purchased his own Bible in 1763, read it diligently, and sprinkled his writings with scriptural quotations. He never formally joined a

—PRINTED FOR—

And Sold by JOHN FISHER, *Stationer.*

BALTIMORE.

Christian denomination, but he often attended Quaker, and sometimes Methodist, services. His reading interests went beyond the Bible to literature in general. He painstakingly compiled a small library, composed essays in his own commonplace book, and wrote poetry.

Mathematics, though, was the subject that stimulated his intellectual curiosity the most. He had unusual abilities with numbers. While a young man, he became locally famous for being able to solve fairly complex computations in his head. He had a special fondness for mathematical puzzles and liked to trade tricky problems with his neighbors.

It was probably during such an exchange with a neighbor that Banneker first saw and then borrowed a watch. The timepiece fascinated him, and he dismantled it to observe its moving parts. Using the watch as a model, Banneker produced a clock made entirely of hand-carved hardwoods. The clock kept accurate time, struck the hours, and was the wonder of the Patapsco valley.

Banneker completed the clock in 1753, when he was twenty-two. His father died six years later, leaving Benjamin the sole owner of the Stout acreage. The rest of the property was divided among Benjamin and his two married sisters. Banneker lived with his mother until she died in 1775. He never married and lived the rest of his life on his well-kept, productive farm. He might have died in obscurity had not the Ellicott brothers bought land adjoining the Banneker farm.

Life's Work

Joseph, Andrew, and John Ellicott brought their large families and the families of several workers to the Patapsco valley in 1771, when Banneker was forty. Before they were fully settled, the Ellicotts and their workers bought food from the existing farms. Andrew Ellicott's young son George and Banneker developed a special friendship. At age fifteen in 1775, George was recognized as a mathematical prodigy, an accomplished surveyor, and a gifted astronomer. With George's encouragement and assistance, Banneker rapidly mastered advanced mathematics and became fascinated with astronomy. In the fall of 1788, George loaned Banneker books on mathematics and astronomy, a telescope, a set of drafting instruments, a lamp, and a large, oval drop-leaf table.

Banneker now spent clear nights in open fields observing the heavens. In cold weather he dressed heavily and wrapped himself in blankets to record his observations. At dawn he returned to his cabin and slept for a few hours. He spent most of the rest of the day at the oval table studying the borrowed books and plotting the movements of the stars. The calculation of a star's location for a particular date could involve as many as ten different algebraic and logarithmic operations.

As he gained a sure grasp of astronomy, Banneker began the ambitious project of calculating an ephemeris—a table showing the positions of the earth, moon, planets, and stars throughout the year. The ephemeris was the basis for projecting eclipses and predicting weather conditions. It was, therefore, the major component of an almanac. He was encouraged in this project by his mentor George and George's cousin Major Andrew Ellicott. Major Ellicott had prepared ephemerides for publication from 1781 through 1786, but the demands of his work as surveyor forced him to abandon the time-consuming calculations. In the summer of 1790, Banneker submitted completed ephemerides for 1791 to three publishers, but none of the editors bought his work. Although discouraged, Banneker began an ephemeris for 1792.

In January of 1791, President George Washington instructed Secretary of State Thomas Jefferson to have the District of Columbia surveyed. On February 2, 1791, Jefferson named Major Ellicott the chief surveyor. Ellicott was to find the true meridian and longitude of the future capital and to prepare a topographical map of the ten-mile square tract of land. Because he was shorthanded, Ellicott turned to Banneker for help. Banneker had no practical experience as a surveyor, but he had mastered the mathematics involved and knew how to work with most of the astronomical instruments.

On February 7, 1791, Banneker—at age fifty-nine—made his first trip outside Baltimore County. During his three-month stay at the site of the future capital, he gained valuable experience as assistant to Major Ellicott. He learned to use the astronomical clock and other instruments new to him. He also kept a resolution to abstain from drinking wine and hard liquor while working with the surveying crew.

Upon his return home, he finished the ephemeris for 1792. Meanwhile, Joseph and George Ellicott had interested the Society of Friends meetings and the antislavery societies in Baltimore and Philadelphia in Banneker. Through their assistance, Banneker's 1792 ephemeris was published by the Baltimore firm of Goddard and Angell. The almanac appeared for sale in stores in Baltimore, Philadelphia, and Alexandria in December, 1791, bearing the title: *Benjamin Banneker's Pennsylvania, Delaware, Maryland and Virginia Almanack and Ephemeris for the Year of Our Lord, 1792*. On the reverse side of the title page the editors called the work "an extraordinary Effort of Genius—a COMPLETE and ACCURATE EPHEMERIS . . . calculated by a sable Descendant of Africa. . . ." The editors argued that the almanac was proof that skin color had no relationship to mental capacity, that all people were alike, and that slavery should be ended. The first four thousand copies quickly sold out, as did a second printing by Goddard and Angell and a condensed edition printed by William Young in Philadelphia.

Banneker prepared an ephemeris that was published in an almanac each year through 1797. The almanacs were extremely popular and sold well. At least twenty-eight editions of these almanacs appeared in those six years.

Starting in 1794, Banneker computed tide tables for Chesapeake Bay, a feature that competing almanacs did not contain.

The elderly astronomer was a dark-skinned man of average height and a full head of thick, white hair. Though portly, he stood erect and carried a long staff. His posture, gentlemanly behavior, and staff gave him a dignified, patriarchal air. Banneker continued to calculate ephemerides through the year 1802. In that year, he turned seventy-one; his capacity for work had diminished, and he was unable to complete the rigorous computations. He died quietly in his home four years later on October 9, 1806.

Summary

Banneker's abilities as a mathematician and astronomer made him famous in his lifetime. There was, however, much more to his fame than his accomplishments themselves. Benjamin Banneker was the son and grandson of Africans. He was a free black in a predominantly white society that almost universally regarded black people as being mentally inferior to whites. Banneker's best-known act—in his lifetime and since—was his correspondence with Thomas Jefferson.

On August 19, 1791, Banneker sent the author of the Declaration of Independence a handwritten copy of his ephemeris and a long letter. Banneker introduced himself as a black man and then eloquently pleaded with Jefferson to use his influence to end the slavery that still kept some of the children of mankind's one Father from enjoying their "inalienable rights." Jefferson responded by expressing the hope that people would soon recognize that circumstances, not natural endowments, kept blacks in a condition that suggested inferiority, but he made no pledge to do anything more than to send Banneker's almanac to abolitionists in France.

Those two letters were printed in the 1793 alamanc and reprinted frequently in abolitionist literature in the nineteenth century. Benjamin Banneker had become a symbol of racial equality because he was an example of black achievement. His name has been invoked over the years in black educational efforts, such as Benjamin Banneker College of Prairie View A & M University at Prairie View, Texas.

Bibliography

Allen, Will W., comp. *Banneker: The Afro-American Astronomer*. Washington, D.C.: Black Heritage Library, 1921. Reprint. Freeport, N.Y.: Books for Libraries Press, 1971. First published in 1921 by the Black Heritage Library Collection, the work is based largely on primary sources but contains a paper by Daniel Murray which advances the undocumented claim that Banneker worked with Major Pierre Charles L'Enfant and had a copy of the city's plans for use after L'Enfant left the capital site in a rage. That myth has been repeated often.

Allen, William G. *Wheatley, Banneker, and Horton*. Boston: D. Laing, 1849. Reprint. Freeport, N.Y.: Books for Libraries Press, 1970. A condensation of an earlier paper based on records held by the Ellicott family.

Armistead, Wilson. *A Tribute for the Negro: Being a Vindication of the Moral, Intellectual, and Religious Capabilities of the Colored Portion of Mankind; with Particular Reference to the African Race*. Manchester: W. Irwin, 1848. Reprint. Miami, Fl.: Mnemosyne, 1969. Abolitionist literature. The material on Banneker consists of a brief biographical sketch and a reprint of the Jefferson correspondence.

Baker, Henry E. "Benjamin Banneker, the Negro Mathematician and Astronomer." *The Journal of Negro History* 3 (April, 1918): 99-118. A fine sketch based upon a rare work prepared by George Ellicott's daughter Martha Ellicott Tyson.

Bedini, Silvio A. *The Life of Benjamin Banneker*. New York: Charles Scribner's Sons, 1971. The best study of Banneker produced yet. Based on careful review of secondary materials, previously unused material from private archives, and Banneker's commonplace book and journal.

Graham, Shirley. *Your Most Humble Servant*. New York: Julian Messner, 1949. Although shelved in the biography section of libraries, this work contains many fictitious characters and events.

Miller, John Chester. *The Wolf by the Ears: Thomas Jefferson and Slavery*. New York: Free Press, 1977. Treats the correspondence between Banneker and Jefferson in the context of Jefferson's life and the slavery problem in the United States.

Paul E. Kuhl

SIR FREDERICK GRANT BANTING

Born: November 14, 1891; Alliston, Ontario, Canada
Died: February 22, 1941; Newfoundland, Canada
Area of Achievement: Medicine
Contribution: Along with Charles Herbert Best, Banting is credited with having discovered insulin, one of the great scientific and humanitarian achievements of the twentieth century.

Early Life

Frederick Grant Banting was born on his parents' farm in Alliston, Ontario, and was of Irish-Scottish extraction. The youngest of five children, Frederick enjoyed the advantages of a boyhood in the country and developed an affection for animals and close ties to nature. At local schools he was considered to be a serious but otherwise undistinguished student, although his hardy upbringing did result in his excelling at sports and his tendency toward pugnacity was a particular asset on the athletic field. An important event in his early childhood was seeing Jane, a childhood friend, die of uncontrolled diabetes mellitus. Although, largely because of his father's encouragement, he had considered becoming a minister, he quickly realized that medicine was his true calling, and he entered the University of Toronto Medical School in 1912.

Banting was about six feet tall and somewhat shy. He had a particularly winning smile and a twinkle in his eye, and although some would characterize his features as "horsey," he was, when dressed up, a handsome man. Banting's five-year medical course at Toronto was shortened because of the war, and he recalled in his writings that he had "a very deficient medical training." Immediately after his graduation, Banting was sent to England. Before he left, he became engaged to his longtime girlfriend, Edith Roach. While serving in England he developed extensive surgical experience dealing with wounds. Six weeks before the end of the war, upon learning that the medical officer of the Forty-sixth Battalion had been wounded, he went immediately to take the wounded doctor's place. Despite receiving a shrapnel wound in his right forearm and orders to return, he went on to the front line and continued serving the wounded until he collapsed from blood loss. The wound in the arm became infected and amputation was threatened. Banting took over the care of his own wound and with a meticulous program of dressing changes and many, many months of persistence, the wound finally healed. For his courage under fire, he received the Military Cross.

When Banting returned to Canada, he decided to enter practice in London, Ontario, because Edith was teaching in a nearby school. On July 1, 1920, Banting opened an office in the house that he bought in the residential area of London. His practice was slow at the outset; his first patient came in

The Nobel Foundation

on July 29. One of his good friends at this time was William Tew, with whom he spent many evenings in the study of medicine. Studying was something that Banting enjoyed: It was a way to pass the time in his quiet practice. He resumed preparation for the difficult exam of Fellowship in the British Royal College of Surgeons. He also began assisting Dr. F. R. Miller of London's Western University, who was a well-known professor of physiology.

Life's Work

On Sunday, October 30, 1920, Banting, in preparing a lecture on the pancreas and on carbohydrate metabolism for physiology students, became aware of how little was known about the pancreas or diabetes. His copy of the November issue of the journal *Surgery, Gynecology, and Obstetrics* had just arrived, and he began to read an article titled "The Relation of the Islets of Langerhans to Diabetes with Special Reference to Cases of Pancreatic Lithiasis," by Moses Barron. Barron, while performing routine autopsies, had come upon cases in which the pancreatic duct had been obstructed by a stone and had found that most of the pancreas had atrophied except for the islet cells. Previous evidence, as well as this new piece of pathological evidence, seemed to suggest that the islet cells were important in secreting directly into the bloodstream something that prevented diabetes. Banting ruminated over these findings through much of the night. Finally, at two o'clock in the morning, it suddenly occurred to him that the experimental ligation of the pancreatic duct and the subsequent degeneration of those parts of the pancreas responsible for external secretion into the duodenum might then result in one's being left with only that part of the pancreas important in the secretion of the internal factor thought to be important in diabetes. That would allow this factor to be isolated without being contaminated by the powerful enzymes, such as trypsin, that the pancreas normally secretes into the duodenum. This thought made Banting tremendously excited, and he discussed his theory with Miller, at Western University, who encouraged him to consult Dr. J. J. R. Macleod, a professor of physiology at the University of Toronto. The interview with Professor Macleod was brief and, as far as Banting was concerned, unsatisfactory. It appeared that Macleod thought him ill-trained for the task he had outlined, and Banting thought that Macleod's scorn was thinly veiled. Macleod did not dismiss Banting outright, however, and left him the option of pursuing his hypothesis at Toronto. Banting returned to London and discussed his options at length with Miller.

At this point, Banting was considering a number of different routes he might take in his life. His practice was picking up and his income was rising, and he was constantly being encouraged by his fiancée to settle down into full-time practice. Sometime during the winter or spring, while Banting continued to debate over the wisdom of moving to Toronto, Edith apparently broke off the engagement with him. This apparently was the turning point in his decision to go to Toronto, where he again met with Macleod to plan the work. It appeared that Macleod was no more impressed than he had been earlier with Banting's knowledge of research, but he consented to Banting's use of the lab. Macleod assigned Charles Herbert Best, a young physiology student, to help Banting in his endeavor. Having given up his instructorship at Western University, sold his house and furnishings in London, and closed his office, Banting had burned his bridges behind him.

For more than a quarter century before Banting undertook his experiments, there was general agreement that the cause of diabetes was the failure of the pancreas to secrete enough of a certain mysterious substance necessary for the proper utilization of carbohydrates as a body fuel. As a result of this failure, the unassimilated sugar was constantly being secreted in the urine, drawing with it tremendous quantities of water and thereby leaving the victim with the triad of tremendous thirst, large volumes of urine, and increasing waste. The problem that had faced physiologists for years, and that had stumped them, was where this mysterious pancreatic secretion resided, as it apparently was not secreted into pancreatic ducts and must therefore be released into the bloodstream directly. Banting and Best began their experiments by ligating the pancreatic ducts of dogs with cat gut. They waited almost seven weeks, which must have been a very nerve-racking period, at which time they opened the dog's abdomen, only to find, to their bitter disappointment, that the pancreas was not atrophied. The cat gut that had been used for ligatures had disintegrated, so that the gland, no longer blocked, did not degenerate. The experiment was repeated, and on July 30 Banting and Best reoperated on the dogs and found the pancreases notably shriveled. They then cut the atrophied organ into small pieces, ground it up, and obtained a crude extract which they then injected into the same dog. By this time the dog had all the symptoms of diabetes, with tremendous sugar in his urine and weight loss. Within a few hours of injecting the substance into the dog, Banting and Best began to see increasing signs of returning strength in the dog, as well as a fall in the blood and urine sugar to normal levels.

This was a very solemn moment. Banting and Best, though quite thrilled with their discovery, were also worried, because it hardly seemed possible that they had achieved, in such a short time and with such crude extracts, what famous scientists had been unable to achieve. Over the next few weeks, Banting and Best refined the techniques both of producing the pancreatic lesion that would allow them to extract this new substance and of improving the method of extraction. They had read that the islets of Langerhans in the fetus were much larger than those in children after birth, and therefore they obtained fetuses from pregnant slaughtered cows and found that the fetal pancreas had oversize islets with a generous supply of this new substance that they termed isletin. When Macleod returned from a long sabbatical in Scotland and was presented with their experimental data, his initial reaction was one of caution. He seems also to have questioned the accuracy of some of the data, and engendered quite a bit of resentment and anger. The memorable part of the interview came when Banting, after relating the problems he had encountered in terms of working conditions, demanded from Macleod a salary, a room in which to work, help in looking after the dogs, and a new floor for the operating room—failing which he would leave. Macleod agreed to Banting's conditions, and Banting was to stay at Toronto. Banting and Best were anxious to play the roles of the first human guinea pigs and injected ten units of insulin into each other's arms and suffered no ill effects. The first chance to test this substance on a human patient came on January 11, 1922, on a fourteen-year-old boy, who had almost reached the end of the life expectancy of a diabetic child. He had high levels of blood sugar and was expected to go into a coma and die within a few days. He was given a small quantity of insulin, injected under the skin, and within a few hours his blood sugar had dropped about twenty-five percent and the sugar in his urine decreased. After ten days of receiving insulin, the boy looked and felt better. When the insulin was stopped, the boy's condition deteriorated.

At Banting's request, James Bertram Collip, an expert in biochemistry, was invited to join the investigation. Things progressed quickly thereafter, and Banting and Best were able to present a paper at the American Physiological Society meeting in New Haven, Connecticut, on December 28, 1921. The world had become aware of their remarkable findings, but unfortunately, as word of their discovery grew, Banting had become increasingly dissatisfied with the state of affairs in the lab and suspicious that Macleod was trying to steal his results. To compound the problem, Collip walked into the lab one day and announced to Banting and Best that he had discovered the active principal in the pancreatic islets, but declined to tell them how he had come to his discovery. The only surviving artifact of this crisis in the lab is an agreement signed by Banting, Best, Collip, and Macleod, dated January 25, 1922, in which all agreed not to take a step which would result in the process of obtaining a pancreatic extract being patented by a commercial firm. Banting became increasingly concerned that he and Best were being treated as technicians while the bulk of the work had been passed on to experts.

In April of 1922, the Toronto group prepared a paper summarizing the entire work to that point. The paper "The Effect Produced on Diabetes by Extracts of Pancreas," was presented by Macleod at the meeting of the Association of American Physicians. On May 22, the Toronto group agreed to collaborate with Eli Lilly and Company, which turned all of its huge resources toward the production of this compound.

Much controversy still exists concerning who should actually receive the credit for discovering insulin. The Nobel assembly, on October 25, voted by secret ballot to award the 1923 prize to Banting and Macleod. As soon as Banting heard that, he became angry at the thought of Macleod being given credit for the discovery. He immediately announced that he would share his prize with Best. Macleod, in turn, after some reflection, elected to share his portion with Collip. Numerous letters were written to the Nobel Committee by various persons, protesting the decision. Nicolas Paulesco in Bucharest had done preliminary experiments with pancreatic extract; had he proceeded more quickly, he might well have received the credit for discovering insulin.

Banting became an important public figure and was much sought-after as a speaker and teacher. The Banting and Best Department of Medical Research at the University of Toronto was separate from the rest of the university; it was Banting's own kingdom, populated by colorful, hard-drinking students and cronies, some of whom were also good scientists.

Banting became more interested in things other than medicine, including the arts, and took up painting. In 1924, Canada's most eligible bachelor was swept off his feet and was married to Marion Robertson, a doctor's daughter from Ontario. The marriage was short-lived and produced one child. In 1934, Banting was honored with a knighthood, becoming Sir Frederick Banting, K.B.E. When the war resumed in 1939, Banting had just been married again, to a technician in his department, and was pressed to serve as coordinating chairman of Canada's medical research wartime effort. While in London in the winter of 1939-1940, he began to write a long account of the discovery of insulin. He returned to Canada in the spring of 1940. On February 20, 1941, he took off from Gander, Newfoundland, on board a Hudson bomber en route to England for a second time. The plane crashed in Newfoundland and Banting died in the wreck. There was much speculation as to the cause of his death and the nature of his mission.

Summary

The contribution of Sir Frederick Grant Banting is fundamental to the present era of medicine inasmuch as our understanding of proteins as molecules with a chemical structure that carries information between cells utilizing specific receptors all came about with the availability of insulin. The discovery of insulin has not by any means eliminated all the morbidity of diabetes, but it certainly has extended the lives of millions of diabetics, in many cases allowing them to live nearly normal lives.

Bibliography

Banting, Frederick G., and C. H. Best. "The Discovery and Preparation of Insulin." *University of Toronto Medical Journal* 1 (1923): 94-98. This account is a matter-of-fact report on the sequence of experiments leading to the discovery of insulin. The report avoids controversy, and the conflicts between Banting and MacLeod are not discussed.

Bayliss, W. M. "Insulin, Diabetes, and Rewards for Discoveries." *Nature* 3, no. 2780 (February 10, 1923): 188-191. An excellent account of the discovery of insulin by another distinguished scientist. Bayliss did some preliminary experiments that, had he pursued them, could have led to his discovering insulin.

Bliss, Michael. *The Discovery of Insulin*. Chicago: University of Chicago Press, 1982. A detailed account of the personalities and events leading to the discovery of insulin, with a short biography of Banting. MacLeod is portrayed in a more favorable light than in other books. This book is the best researched and referenced book on the subject.

Burtness, H. I., and E. F. Cain. "A Thirty-fifth Anniversary of Insulin Therapy." *Diabetes* 7 (January/February, 1958): 59-61. A general overview of the impact of insulin on the therapy of diabetes. The almost normal lifestyle and longevity of patients with diabetes in the present day and age is in striking contrast to preinsulin days.

Harris, Seale. *Banting's Miracle: The Story of the Discoverer of Insulin*. Philadelphia: J. B. Lippincott and Co., 1946. A biography of Banting that is very biased in favor of Banting and against Macleod. It presents a good picture of Banting's personal life.

Macleod, John James Rickard. "History of the Researches Leading to the Discovery of Insulin." *Bulletin of the History of Medicine* 52 (Fall, 1978): 295-312. This is MacLeod's own account of the events leading to the discovery of insulin. A dry, factual account, it avoids the controversy between MacLeod and Banting.

Pratt, Joseph H. "A Reappraisal of Researches Leading to the Discovery of Insulin." *Journal of the History of Medicine* 9 (1954): 281-289. Another viewpoint on the controversy surrounding the discovery of insulin. Clearly, the researchers into the history of the discovery of insulin have all come away with different conclusions—this one portrays MacLeod as less of a villain than other reports.

Wrenshall, G. A., G. Hetenyi, and W. R. Feasby. *The Story of Insulin: Forty Years of Success Against Diabetes*. London: The Bodley Head, 1962. An account of insulin, its discovery and production, that is well written and highly readable. This is perhaps the fairest and most objective review of the events at Toronto.

Abraham Verghese
James A. Cowan